comprehensive
mathematics practice answers

C. Oliver
Thomas Sumpter School, Scunthorpe

A. Ledsham
King Edward Sixth Form College, Stourbridge

R. Elvin
Head of Mathematics, Thomas Sumpter School, Scunthorpe

Oxford University Press 1981

Oxford University Press, Walton Street, Oxford OX2 6DP

London Glasgow New York Toronto
Delhi Bombay Calcutta Madras Karachi
Nairobi Dar es Salaam Cape Town Salisbury
Kuala Lumpur Singapore Hong Kong Tokyo
Melbourne Auckland

and associate companies in
Beirut Berlin Ibadan Mexico City

ISBN 0 19 833669 1

Printed in Great Britain by
The Thetford Press, Thetford, Norfolk

answers

BOOK 1   PART 1

Exercise 1   *page 1*

1. (a) Mary, William, John   (b) Jane, Anne, Peter
2. (a) 6, 8, 10, 12, 14   (b) 18, 20, 22, 24, 26
   (c) 34, 36, 38, 40, 42   (d) 90, 92, 94, 96, 98
   (e) 102, 104, 106, 108, 110
3. (a) 7, 9, 11, 13, 15   (b) 15, 17, 19, 21, 23
   (c) 33, 35, 37, 39, 41   (d) 71, 73, 75, 77, 79
   (e) 119, 121, 123, 125, 127

Exercise 2   *page 1*

1. (a) C (b) A (c) B
2. (a) R (b) R (c) R, S (d) R, T (e) N (f) R (g) N (h) S
   (i) R, T (j) R, S, T
4. (a) 9 (b) 16 (c) 25 (d) 100 (e) 10 000
5. (a) 4 (b) 9 (c) 16 (d) 25 (e) 36 (f) square

Exercise 3   *page 2*

1. C 2. 2, 3, 5, 7, 11, 13, 17, 19, 23, 29 3. (a), (c), (f), (h), (i), (l)

Exercise 4   *page 2*

1. 22 m, 26 m
2. (a) 10, 12, 14, 16, 18   (b) 15, 18, 21, 24, 27   (c) 60, 72, 84, 96, 108
   (d) 30, 25, 20, 15, 10   (e) 42, 36, 30, 24, 18   (f) 28, 21, 14, 7, 0
   (g) 28, 33, 38, 43, 48   (h) 29, 35, 41, 47, 53   (i) 24, 20, 16, 12, 8
   (j) 58, 50, 42, 34, 26   3. 27
4. (a) 16, 32, 64   (b) 256, 1024, 4096   (c) 2000, 20 000, 200 000
   (d) 4, 2, 1   (e) 9, 3, 1   (f) 25, 5, 1
5. (a) 9, (b) 10 (c) 14 (d) 85 (e) 64 (f) 55 (g) 3 (h) 6
   (i) 50 (j) 15 (k) 16 (l) 9

Exercise 5   *page 3*

1. twelve 2. fifteen 3. thirty-six 4. ninety-one
5. one hundred and fifty 6. three hundred and forty
7. three hundred and forty-five 8. two hundred and ten
9. two hundred and seventeen 10. five hundred and eight
11. six hundred and one 12. two thousand three hundred
13. two thousand three hundred and seventy
14. three thousand six hundred and seventy
15. three thousand six hundred and seventy-eight
16. seven thousand two hundred and ten
17. seven thousand two hundred and fifteen
18. seven thousand two hundred and three
19. four thousand five hundred and four

20. four thousand and twenty-four   21. three thousand and thirty-seven
22. three thousand and thirty   23. eight thousand and twenty
24. eight thousand and seven   25. nine thousand and one
26. (a) three hundred and nine metres
    (b) eighty-three kilometres   (c) five hundred and fifty-nine kilometres
27. two thousand four hundred and fourteen metres
28. (a) four thousand eight hundred and fifty-seven kilometres
    (b) seven thousand two hundred and seventy kilometres
    (c) nine thousand five hundred and fifteen kilometres

Exercise 6 *page 3*

1. 17   2. 19   3. 45   4. 73   5. 190   6. 460
7. 467   8. 810   9. 812   10. 704   11. 901   12. 6500
13. 6520   14. 9130   15. 9133   16. 3610   17. 3619   18. 3602
19. 8706   20. 8091   21. 1056   22. 1050   23. 4010   24. 4004
25. 8011   26. 736   27. 887   28. 9121   29. 7206   30. 1085

Exercise 7 *page 4*

1. 1   2. 6   3. 5   4. 3   5. 7   6. 30
7. 50   8. 300   9. 900   10. 500   11. 6   12. 2
13. 7   14. 2   15. 70   16. 10   17. 60   18. 50
19. 900   20. 100   21. 300   22. 200   23. 8000   24. 1000
25. 9000

Exercise 8 *page 4*

1. 70, 71, 72, 73, 75   2. 40, 45, 50, 54, 55
3. 112, 113, 121, 123, 132   4. 99, 109, 110, 112, 120
5. 412, 421, 423, 432, 433   6. 504, 505, 530, 534, 540
7. 678, 687, 768, 786, 876   8. 2123, 2132, 2231, 2312, 2321
9. 1006, 1016, 1060, 1061, 1106   10. 4004, 4040, 4044, 4400, 4404
11. 88, 89, 90, 98, 99   12. 80, 88, 108, 118, 180
13. 103, 113, 123, 130, 133   14. 215, 220, 225, 250, 255
15. 605, 606, 650, 660, 665   16. 56, 55, 54, 45, 44
17. 119, 109, 104, 99, 94   18. 155, 150, 125, 120, 105
19. 352, 350, 342, 332, 330   20. 444, 441, 440, 414, 404

Exercise 9 *page 5*

1. 532, 235   2. 943, 349   3. 861, 168   4. 553, 355
5. 760, 607   6. 6543, 3456   7. 9741, 1479   8. 8521, 1258
9. 7511, 1157   10. 6633, 3366   11. 5320, 2035   12. 9700, 7009

Exercise 10 *page 5*

1. 40   2. 70   3. 150   4. 190   5. 100   6. 240
7. 430   8. 520   9. 690   10. 200   11. 500   12. 1260
13. 1550   14. 3170   15. 6320   16. 5100   17. 8500   18. 7000
19. 23 170   20. 35 470   21. 46 200   22. 70 500   23. 53 000   24. 80 000
25. 99 010

Exercise 11 *page 5*

1. 3   2. 5   3. 7   4. 6 r 5   5. 5 r 4   6. 7 r 3
7. 12   8. 16   9. 37   10. 82   11. 20   12. 90
13. 44 r 5   14. 63 r 8   15. 30 r 7   16. 40 r 2   17. 132   18. 478
19. 230   20. 520   21. 700   22. 517 r 6   23. 307 r 8   24. 420 r 4
25. 900 r 1

Exercise 12 *page 5*

1. 300   2. 900   3. 1300   4. 1600   5. 1000   6. 2500
7. 5100   8. 7800   9. 3000   10. 6000   11. 12 400   12. 23 700
13. 51 900   14. 70 800   15. 63 000   16. 81 000   17. 40 000   18. 90 000
19. 10 000   20. 99 900

Exercise 13   *page 5*   **1.** 2   **2.** 6   **3.** 8   **4.** 8 r 50   **5.** 8 r 53   **6.** 7 r 64
7. 7 r 4   **8.** 5 r 2   **9.** 32   **10.** 97   **11.** 97 r 10   **12.** 46 r 80
13. 46 r 83   **14.** 51 r 62   **15.** 93 r 75   **16.** 41 r 18   **17.** 13 r 84   **18.** 37 r 25
19. 37 r 5   **20.** 51 r 7   **21.** 50 r 7   **22.** 20 r 8   **23.** 20 r 30   **24.** 80 r 70

Exercise 14   *page 6*   **1.** £540   **2.** 200 cm, 2 m   **3.** 9500 cm, 95 m
4. (a) 12   (b) 5   **5.** (a) 13   (b) 18

Exercise 15   *page 6*   **1, 2** and **3.** $26 \times 10 = 260$ **4, 5** and **6.** $260 \div 10 = 26$
7, 8 and **9.** $70 \times 10 = 700$ **10, 11** and **12.** $700 \div 10 = 70$
13, 14 and **15.** $145 \times 10 = 1450$ **16, 17** and **18.** $1450 \div 10 = 145$
19, 20 and **21.** $240 \times 10 = 2400$ **22, 23** and **24.** $2400 \div 10 = 240$
25, 26 and **27.** $400 \times 10 = 4000$ **28, 29** and **30.** $4000 \div 10 = 400$
31, 32 and **33.** $13 \times 100 = 1300$ **34, 35** and **36.** $1300 \div 100 = 13$
37, 38 and **39.** $50 \times 100 = 5000$ **40, 41** and **42.** $5000 \div 100 = 50$

Exercise 16   *page 7*   **1.** (c)   **2.** (d)   **3.** (a)   **4.** (b)   **5.** (a)   **6.** (d)   **7.** (b)   **8.** (b)
9. (c)   **10.** (b)   **11.** (b)   **12.** (a)   **13.** (a)   **14.** (d)   **15.** (d)   **16.** (b)
17. (a)   **18.** (c)   **19.** (a)   **20.** (c)   **21.** (d)   **22.** (b)   **23.** (a)   **24.** (c)
25. (a)   **26.** (d)   **27.** (c)   **28.** (b)   **29.** (a)   **30.** (b)

Exercise 17   *page 8*   **1.** (b)   **2.** (c)   **3.** (b)   **4.** (b)   **5.** (c)   **6.** (a)   **7.** (c)   **8.** (b)
9. (a)   **10.** (a)   **11.** (a)   **12.** (c)   **13.** (a)   **14.** (a)   **15.** (b)   **16.** (b)
17. (a)   **18.** (a)   **19.** (c)   **20.** (b)   **21.** (a)   **22.** (c)   **23.** (b)   **24.** (c)
25. (b)

Exercise 18   *page 9*   **1.** (a)   **2.** (c)   **3.** (a)   **4.** (b)   **5.** (b)   **6.** (b)   **7.** (c)   **8.** (b)
9. (a)   **10.** (b)

Exercise 19   *page 10*   **1.** (b)   **2.** (a)   **3.** (b)   **4.** (d)   **5.** (a)   **6.** (b)   **7.** (b)   **8.** (c)
9. (d)   **10.** (a)   **11.** (d)   **12.** (c)   **13.** (b)   **14.** (a)   **15.** (a)   **16.** (c)
17. (b)   **18.** (a)   **19.** (a)   **20.** (c)

Exercise 20   *page 10*   **1.** (a)   **2.** (c)   **3.** (b)   **4.** (a)   **5.** (a)   **6.** (b)   **7.** (c)   **8.** (b)
9. (b)   **10.** (a)   **11.** (b)   **12.** (c)   **13.** (b)   **14.** (a)   **15.** (c)   **16.** (a)
17. (b)   **18.** (a)   **19.** (b)   **20.** (b)

Exercise 21   *page 11*   **1.** (b)   **2.** (a)   **3.** (b)   **4.** (c)   **5.** (a)   **6.** (b)   **7.** (c)   **8.** (a)
9. (a)   **10.** (b)

Exercise 22   *page 11*   **1.** 9   **2.** 42, 18   **3.** 19p   **4.** 12 s   **5.** 33, 63
6. 2nd July, 29th July   **7.** 883, 27   **8.** 17
9. Peter by 4 points   **10.** via Widnes and Warrington by 6 km

Exercise 23   *page 12*   **3, 5** and **8** are not magic squares

Exercise 24   *page 13*

1.
2	7	6
9	5	1
4	3	8

2.
6	12	3
4	7	10
11	2	8

3.
9	5	4
1	6	11
8	7	3

4.
7	12	5
6	8	10
11	4	9

5.
14	11	7	2
1	8	12	13
4	5	9	16
15	10	6	3

6.
10	5	17	6
8	15	3	12
7	16	4	11
13	2	14	9

7.
6	12	11	9
17	3	4	14
5	15	16	2
10	8	7	13

8.
10	5	8	11
3	16	13	2
15	4	1	14
6	9	12	7

9.
```
 3 22  1 20 19
24  8 15 16  2
17 21 13  5  9
14 10 11 18 12
 7  4 25  6 23
```
10.
```
 8 25 18 15  4
 7 11 22  9 21
26 12 14 16  2
 5 19  6 17 23
24  3 10 13 20
```

Exercise 25 *page 13*

1. 34 **2.** 34 **3.** 34 **4.** 36 **5.** 34 **6.** 32 **7.** 34 **8.** 24
9. 44 **10.** 34 **11.** 26 **12.** 34 **13.** 42 **14.** 40 **15.** 34 **16.** 34
17. 34 **18.** 28 **19.** 34 **20.** 34 **21.** 34: the sum of each row, each
column, and each diagonal is 34.

Exercise 26 *page 14*

1. 100 **2.** 100 **3.** 100 **4.** 36

Exercise 28 *page 15*

1. 4 years **2.** 8 years **3.** 12 years **4.** 18 years **5.** 23 years
6. 29 years **7.** 33 years **8.** 40 years **9.** 47 years **10.** 52 years
11. 59 years **12.** 67 years **13.** 76 years **14.** 80 years **15.** 92 years
16. 1981 **17.** 1977 **18.** 1975 **19.** 1971 **20.** 1960
21. 1957 **22.** 1952 **23.** 1946 **24.** 1939 **25.** 1935
26. 1921 **27.** 1918 **28.** 1909 **29.** 1897 **30.** 1893

Exercise 29 *page 16*

1. 27 **2.** 46 **3.** 36 **4.** 28 **5.** 37
6. 9 **7.** 28 **8.** 33 **9.** 14 **10.** 27
11. 29th Jan **12.** 27th Jan **13.** 21st Mar **14.** 17th Jan **15.** 16th May
16. 28th Jan **17.** 13th Jan **18.** 14th Jan **19.** 4th July **20.** 5th Aug
21. 3rd Feb **22.** 4th Feb **23.** 2nd Apr **24.** 5th Feb **25.** 9th Feb

Exercise 30 *page 16*

1. 75 **2.** 84 **3.** 87 **4.** 79 **5.** 92 **6.** 97 **7.** 88 **8.** 101
9. 98 **10.** 109 **11.** 120 **12.** 115 **13.** 130 **14.** 134 **15.** 123 **16.** 129
17. 80 **18.** 55 **19.** 54 **20.** 65

Exercise 31 *page 17*

1. 11.30 h **2.** 10.15 h **3.** 09.20 h **4.** 07.25 h **5.** 08.45 h
6. 05.40 h **7.** 02.10 h **8.** 03.50 h **9.** 01.55 h **10.** 04.00 h
11. 06.05 h **12.** 15.30 h **13.** 14.15 h **14.** 18.10 h **15.** 16.25 h
16. 19.45 h **17.** 17.35 h **18.** 13.40 h **19.** 20.20 h **20.** 21.55 h
21. 19.00 h **22.** 18.25 h **23.** 15.05 h **24.** 21.50 h **25.** 20.00 h
26. 22.20 h **27.** 23.15 h **28.** 22.55 h **29.** 23.35 h **30.** 24.00 h

Exercise 32 *page 17*

1. 11.15 a.m. **2.** 10.20 a.m. **3.** 9.10 a.m. **4.** 8.30 a.m.
5. 4.25 a.m. **6.** 2.45 a.m. **7.** 3.40 a.m. **8.** 1.50 a.m.
9. 5.35 a.m. **10.** 7.00 a.m. **11.** 12.30 a.m. **12.** 2.30 p.m.
13. 4.10 p.m. **14.** 5.15 p.m. **15.** 6.45 p.m. **16.** 1.50 p.m.
17. 3.40 p.m. **18.** 4.35 p.m. **19.** 7.05 p.m. **20.** 8.15 p.m.
21. 9.20 p.m. **22.** 11.00 p.m. **23.** 10.30 p.m. **24.** 10.05 p.m.
25. 11.25 p.m. **26.** 11.50 p.m. **27.** 8.55 p.m. **28.** 9.45 p.m.
29. 7.40 p.m. **30.** 6.05 p.m.

Exercise 33 *page 17*

1. 35 min **2.** 1 h 15 min **3.** 2 h 30 min **4.** 2 h 40 min
5. 25 min **6.** 3 h 35 min **7.** 5 h 25 min **8.** 1 h 15 min
9. 40 min **10.** 25 min **11.** 1 h 40 min **12.** 2 h 15 min
13. 1 h 5 min **14.** 45 min **15.** 4 h 5 min **16.** 20 min
17. 1 h 35 min **18.** 25 min
19. 1 h 5 min, 1 h 30 min, 2 h, 2 h 20 min, 2 h 35 min

20. 35 min, 50 min, 1 h 10 min, 1 h 30 min, 2 h 15 min
21. (a) 8.10 a.m., 6.05 p.m., 8.50 a.m., 6.30 p.m.
    (b) 08.15 h, 20 min, 25 min, 15.50 h, 20 min
    (c) 11.05 h, 20 min, 5 min, 15.55 h, 4 h 25 min
22. (a) 9.20 a.m., 6.30 p.m., 8.25 a.m., 5.30 p.m.
    (b) 13.50 h, 25 min, 15 min, 17.20 h, 50 min
    (c) 12.50 h, 30 min, 40 min, 18.30 h, 4 h 20 min

Revision exercise A
page 19

1. 32 min, 28 min　　2. 128 km　　3. 300 cm, 3 m　　4. 600 p, £6
5. The triangular numbers reappear　　6.　1　32　28　8　7　35
8. (a) 26　(b) 47　(c) 35　(d) 26　　　　　10　24　21　17　12　27
   (e) 38　(f) 28th April　　　　　　　　　34　11　18　22　23　3
   (g) 25th April　(h) 17th April　　　　　33　14　15　19　26　4
   (i) 14th June　(j) 4th May　　　　　　31　25　20　16　13　6
   (k) 1st May　(l) 7th December　　　　　2　5　9　29　30　36

BOOK 1　PART 2

Exercise 34　*page 20*

1. $\frac{3}{4}$　2. $\frac{5}{6}$　3. $\frac{4}{5}$　4. $\frac{2}{3}$　5. $\frac{1}{4}$　6. $\frac{2}{3}$　7. $\frac{3}{4}$　8. $\frac{1}{3}$
9. $\frac{2}{3}$　10. $\frac{1}{3}$

Exercise 35　*page 21*

1. (c)　2. (b)　3. (b)　4. (b)　5. (c)　6. (b)　7. (a)　8. (b)
9. (b)　10. (c)

Exercise 36　*page 22*

1. (c)　2. (b)　3. (d)　4. (d)　5. (a)　6. (d)　7. (b)　8. (c)
9. (a)　10. (a)　11. (b)　12. (b)　13. (a)　14. (c)　15. (b)　16. (b)
17. (b)　18. (a)　19. (c)　20. (a)　21. (b)　22. (a)　23. (c)　24. (a)
25. (a)

Exercise 38　*page 23*

1. $\frac{2}{6}$　2. $\frac{6}{8}$　3. $\frac{4}{8}$　4. $\frac{6}{15}$　5. $\frac{4}{20}$　6. $\frac{12}{32}$　7. $\frac{5}{30}$　8. $\frac{25}{40}$
9. $\frac{18}{30}$　10. $\frac{12}{18}$　11. $\frac{9}{36}$　12. $\frac{12}{60}$　13. $\frac{2}{16}$　14. $\frac{14}{20}$　15. $\frac{3}{36}$　16. $\frac{12}{15}$
17. $\frac{4}{36}$　18. $\frac{20}{28}$　19. $\frac{15}{40}$　20. $\frac{25}{30}$　21. $\frac{18}{24}$　22. $\frac{14}{35}$　23. $\frac{32}{40}$　24. $\frac{24}{36}$
25. $\frac{15}{60}$　26. $\frac{2}{3}$　27. $\frac{5}{6}$　28. $\frac{3}{5}$　29. $\frac{7}{12}$　30. $\frac{4}{5}$　31. $\frac{8}{9}$　32. $\frac{1}{8}$
33. $\frac{3}{7}$　34. $\frac{4}{5}$　35. $\frac{1}{4}$　36. $\frac{3}{4}$　37. $\frac{4}{5}$　38. $\frac{9}{10}$　39. $\frac{7}{12}$　40. $\frac{5}{6}$
41. $\frac{7}{11}$　42. $\frac{5}{8}$　43. $\frac{5}{12}$　44. $\frac{7}{12}$　45. $\frac{8}{9}$　46. $\frac{5}{6}$　47. $\frac{1}{9}$　48. $\frac{5}{6}$
49. $\frac{4}{9}$　50. $\frac{3}{4}$　51. $\frac{1}{2}$　52. $\frac{3}{4}$　53. $\frac{3}{8}$　54. $\frac{5}{12}$　55. $\frac{4}{15}$　56. $\frac{1}{4}$
57. $\frac{2}{3}$　58. $\frac{4}{5}$　59. $\frac{3}{4}$　60. $\frac{7}{20}$　61. $\frac{5}{15}$　62. $\frac{12}{20}$　63. $\frac{25}{30}$　64. $\frac{35}{60}$
65. $\frac{9}{20}$　66. $\frac{5}{30}$　67. $\frac{16}{24}$　68. $\frac{55}{60}$　69. $\frac{24}{60}$　70. $\frac{15}{100}$

Exercise 39　*page 24*

1. $1\frac{1}{6}$　2. $1\frac{1}{8}$　3. $1\frac{2}{3}$　4. $1\frac{3}{7}$　5. $1\frac{5}{6}$　6. $1\frac{4}{5}$　7. $1\frac{5}{8}$　8. $1\frac{7}{10}$
9. $1\frac{3}{11}$　10. $1\frac{5}{12}$　11. $1\frac{1}{4}$　12. $1\frac{2}{3}$　13. $1\frac{3}{5}$　14. $1\frac{1}{3}$　15. $1\frac{1}{4}$　16. $1\frac{2}{3}$
17. $1\frac{3}{5}$　18. $1\frac{1}{2}$　19. $1\frac{2}{3}$　20. $1\frac{2}{3}$　21. $2\frac{1}{2}$　22. $2\frac{1}{4}$　23. $2\frac{2}{3}$　24. $2\frac{4}{5}$

25. $2\frac{1}{4}$ 26. $2\frac{3}{5}$ 27. $2\frac{1}{2}$ 28. $2\frac{2}{3}$ 29. 2   30. 3   31. $3\frac{1}{3}$ 32. $3\frac{1}{4}$

33. $3\frac{3}{4}$ 34. $3\frac{1}{2}$ 35. $3\frac{2}{3}$ 36. $4\frac{1}{2}$ 37. $4\frac{2}{3}$ 38. $4\frac{1}{4}$ 39. $5\frac{1}{4}$ 40. $5\frac{1}{2}$

41. $\frac{5}{4}$ 42. $\frac{10}{9}$ 43. $\frac{7}{5}$ 44. $\frac{11}{8}$ 45. $\frac{12}{7}$ 46. $\frac{13}{10}$ 47. $\frac{19}{12}$ 48. $\frac{15}{8}$

49. $\frac{7}{3}$ 50. $\frac{11}{5}$ 51. $\frac{11}{4}$ 52. $\frac{13}{5}$ 53. $\frac{16}{5}$ 54. $\frac{7}{2}$ 55. $\frac{16}{5}$ 56. $\frac{11}{3}$

57. $\frac{17}{4}$ 58. $\frac{23}{5}$ 59. $\frac{16}{3}$ 60. $\frac{27}{5}$ 61. $\frac{29}{5}$ 62. $\frac{23}{4}$ 63. $\frac{13}{2}$ 64. $\frac{19}{3}$

65. $\frac{15}{2}$ 66. $\frac{3}{1}$ 67. $\frac{8}{1}$ 68. $\frac{15}{1}$ 69. $\frac{40}{1}$ 70. $\frac{1}{1}$

Exercise 40   *page 25*

1. 0·5   2. 0·2   3. 0·07   4. 0·09   5. 0·02
6. 0·05   7. 0·06   8. 0·4   9. 0·1   10. 0·6
11. 0·8   12. 0·2   13. 0·05   14. 0·07   15. 0·01
16. 0·006   17. 0·005   18. 0·002   19. 0·03   20. 0·04
21. 0·006   22. 0·007   23. 0·004   24. 0·006   25. 0·003

Exercise 41   *page 25*

1. 5, 5·02, 5·2, 5·22   2. 4, 4·03, 4·3, 4·33
3. 7, 7·004, 7·04, 7·044, 7·4, 7·44   4. 8, 8·005, 8·05, 8·055, 8·5, 8·55
5. 3, 3·001, 3·01, 3·011, 3·1, 3·11   6. 0·53, 5·03, 5·3, 5·33
7. 0·72, 7·02, 7·2, 7·22   8. 0·65, 6·05, 6·5, 6·55
9. 0·324, 3·024, 3·204, 3·24, 32·4   10. 0·561, 5·061, 5·601, 5·61, 56·1
11. 0·483, 4·083, 4·803, 4·83, 48·03, 48·3
12. 0·275, 2·075, 2·705, 2·75, 27·05, 27·5

Exercise 42   *page 25*

1. 3·56, 65·3   2. 1·48, 84·1   3. 2·39, 93·2   4. 4·57, 75·4
5. 0·25, 52·0   6. 0·67, 76·0   7. 1·235, 532·1   8. 4·567, 765·4
9. 3·489, 984·3   10. 1·356, 653·1   11. 2·478, 874·2   12. 0·235, 532·0
13. 0·178, 871·0   14. 0·034, 430·0   15. 0·079, 970·0

Exercise 43   *page 26*

1. 32·5   2. 53·6   3. 18·4   4. 40·5   5. 20·8   6. 54
7. 82   8. 91   9. 2·6   10. 5·7   11. 8·9   12. 3
13. 9   14. 1   15. 0·3   16. 0·7   17. 4·25   18. 6·41
19. 1·18   20. 4·02   21. 1·05   22. 0·04   23. 0·09   24. 0·54
25. 0·17   26. 45·3   27. 62·7   28. 12·1   29. 50·8   30. 90·6
31. 6·4   32. 3·8   33. 0·5   34. 0·2   35. 36   36. 92
37. 55   38. 4   39. 9   40. 30   41. 80   42. 10
43. 527   44. 394   45. 122   46. 203   47. 606   48. 520
49. 390   50. 110

Exercise 44   *page 26*

1. 0·56   2. 0·32   3. 0·97   4. 0·435   5. 0·158
6. 0·216   7. 0·309   8. 0·5   9. 0·8   10. 0·2
11. 2·54   12. 6·71   13. 9·57   14. 5·06   15. 3·2
16. 7·5   17. 9·9   18. 0·019   19. 0·083   20. 0·055
21. 0·03   22. 0·07   23. 0·01   24. 0·005   25. 0·002
26. 0·352   27. 0·816   28. 0·405   29. 0·201   30. 0·37
31. 0·62   32. 0·5   33. 1·25   34. 2·36   35. 0·0534
36. 0·0995   37. 0·0474   38. 0·0108   39. 0·058   40. 0·036
41. 0·015   42. 0·0027   43. 0·0061   44. 0·0032   45. 0·0005
46. 0·0008   47. 0·0004   48. 0·008   49. 0·003   50. 0·001

Exercise 45   *page 26*

1, 2 and 3. 2·6 × 10 = 26   4, 5 and 6. 3·25 × 10 = 32·5
7, 8 and 9. 5·42 × 100 = 542   10, 11 and 12. 4·8 × 100 = 480
13, 14 and 15. 18·6 ÷ 10 = 1·86   16, 17 and 18. 3·41 ÷ 10 = 0·341
19 and 20. 61·5 ÷ 100 = 0·615

Exercise 46 *page 27*   1. (b)   2. (a)   3. (d)   4. (b)   5. (c)   6. (b)   7. (a)   8. (a)
9. (d)   10. (c)

Exercise 47 *page 27*   1. (b)   2. (a)   3. (a)   4. (c)   5. (b)   6. (a)   7. (a)   8. (c)
9. (b)   10. (a)   11. (b)   12. (b)   13. (a)   14. (b)   15. (a)   16. (b)
17. (c)   18. (c)

Exercise 48 *page 28*   1. (a)   2. (b)   3. (b)   4. (d)   5. (c)   6. (d)   7. (a)   8. (a)
9. (c)   10. (b)   11. (d)   12. (a)   13. (c)   14. (b)   15. (d)   16. (a)
17. (c)   18. (c)   19. (d)   20. (a)

Exercise 49 *page 28*   1. (b)   2. (a)   3. (a)   4. (c)   5. (a)   6. (a)   7. (b)   8. (b)
9. (c)   10. (c)   11. (a)   12. (b)   13. (c)   14. (a)   15. (b)

Exercise 50 *page 29*   1. (b)   2. (b)   3. (a)   4. (c)   5. (b)   6. (a)   7. (a)   8. (c)
9. (b)   10. (a)   11. (b)   12. (c)   13. (a)   14. (b)   15. (b)   16. (a)
17. (c)   18. (b)   19. (a)   20. (c)

Exercise 51 *page 30*   1. 1 m   2. 5 m   3. 11 m   4. 1·75 kg   5. £2·45
6. yes, two short sides and one long side   7. yes, 67·8 km

Revision exercise B 1. (d)   2. (b)   3. (a)   4. (c)   5. (c)   6. (d)   7. (a)   8. (d)
page 31   9. 120 g   10. 3·9 g   11. 120 cm, 1·2 m, 25 m   12. £8·40, £1·60
13. 50.7 s, 0.8 s   14. 0·6 cm, 6 mm   15. 0·75 m by 0·5 m, 75 cm by 50 cm

---

BOOK 1   PART 3

Exercise 52 *page 32*   1. 45°   2. 135°   3. 180°   4. 270°   5. 225°   6. 90°
7. 45°   8. 135°   9. 90°   10. 135°   11. 270°   12. 180°
13. 225°   14. 45°   15. 135°   16. 180°   17. 45°   18. 225°
19. 135°   20. 90°

Exercise 53 *page 33*   1. 90°   2. 30°   3. 120°   4. 60°   5. 60°   6. 180°
7. 150°   8. 150°

Exercise 54 *page 34*   1. 60°   2. 30°   3. 90°   4. 120°   5. 180°   6. 90°
7. 120°   8. 150°   9. 180°   10. 150°   11. 270°   12. 210°
13. 30°, 45°, 60°, 90°, 120°, 135°, 180°, 270°
14. 30°, 45°, 60°, 90°, 120°, 180°
15. 45°, 90°, 180°, 45°, 135°, 90°, 45°

Exercise 55 *page 35*   1. 80°   2. 60°   3. 40°   4. 75°   5. 55°   6. 45°
7. 25°   8. 5°   9. 78°   10. 54°   11. 18°   12. 24°
13. $41\frac{1}{2}$°   14. $7\frac{1}{2}$°   15. 62·5°   16. 150°   17. 140°   18. 120°
19. 100°   20. 90°   21. 10°   22. 50°   23. 70°   24. 175°
25. 165°   26. 135°   27. $112\frac{1}{2}$°   28. 75°   29. 25°   30. 82·5°

Exercise 56 *page 35*   1. $Q\hat{X}Y$ 2. $M\hat{X}Y$, $L\hat{X}Y$
3. $L\hat{M}N$, $M\hat{N}L$, $M\hat{L}N$ 4. $P\hat{Q}R$, $Q\hat{P}R$, $P\hat{R}S$

5. XŴZ, ZX̂Y, XŶZ, XẐY   6. PÔR, QR̂S, PŜR, SP̂Q

7. MK̂L, KL̂M, KM̂N, KN̂M   8. XŴZ, WX̂Z, ZX̂Y, WẐX

9. SP̂R, PQ̂S, PR̂Q, QX̂R   10. KN̂L, LK̂M, NL̂M, MŶN

Exercise 57 *page 37*

1. (a) $10°, 20°, 30°, 50°, 80°$ (b) $90°, 100°, 110°, 120°, 140°$
   (c) $150°, 170°, 180°, 5°, 15°$ (d) $35°, 65°, 75°, 85°, 105°$
   (e) $115°, 125°, 145°, 165°, 10°$ (f) $30°, 40°, 60°, 70°, 80°$
   (g) $90°, 100°, 130°150°, 160°$ (h) $170°, 180°, 15°, 35°, 55°$
   (i) $65°, 75°, 95°, 105°, 115°$ (j) $145°, 165°, 175°$
2. (a) $4°, 7°, 13°, 18°, 22°$ (b) $26°, 31°, 44°, 57°, 69°$
   (c) $74°, 86°, 93°, 108°, 114°$ (d) $127°, 134°, 148°, 157°, 162°$
   (e) $171°, 177°, 3°, 9°, 18°$ (f) $23°, 32°, 46°, 53°, 66°$
   (g) $72°, 87°, 94°, 106°, 111°$ (h) $123°, 136°, 149°, 154°, 158°$
   (i) $162°, 167°, 173°, 176°$
3. (a) $35°, 40°, 45°, 55°, 70°$ (b) $95°, 130°, 155°, 160°, 175°$
   (c) $6°, 12°, 24°, 49°, 64°$ (d) $81°, 103°, 119°, 146°, 151°$
   (e) $166°, 169°, 5°, 20°, 25°$ (f) $50°, 85°, 110°, 125°, 135°$
   (g) $140°, 145°, 11°, 14°, 29°$ (h) $34°, 61°, 77°, 99°, 116°$
   (i) $131°, 156°, 168°, 174°$

Exercise 58 *page 39*

1. $30°$ 2. $50°$ 3. $55°$ 4. $75°$ 5. $25°$ 6. $60°$ 7. $70°$ 8. $40°$
9. $45°$ 10. $35°$ 11. $140°$ 12. $130°$ 13. $135°$ 14. $145°$ 15. $105°$ 16. $120°$
17. $100°$ 18. $160°$ 19. $165°$ 20. $125°$ 21. $50°$ 22. $60°, 30°$ 23. $45°, 45°$
24. $135°$ 25. $60°, 120°$ 26. $135°, 90°$

Exercise 60 *page 45*

1. $80°$ 2. $70°$ 3. $90°$ 4. $30°$ 5. $80°$ 6. $60°$ 7. $110°$ 8. $100°$
9. $30°$ 10. $50°$

Exercise 61 *page 47*

1. $050°$ 2. $080°$ 3. $120°$ 4. $160°$ 5. $220°$ 6. $250°$ 7. $230°$ 8. $260°$
9. $190°$ 10. $180°$ 11. $320°$ 12. $350°$ 13. $330°$ 14. $290°$ 15. $270°$ 16. $300°$

Exercise 63 *page 48*

1. 20 m, $150°$ 2. 70 m, $135°$ 3. 70 km, $045°$
4. 175 km, $060°$ 5. 200 km, $240°$ 6. 10 m, $240°$

Exercise 64 *page 50*

1. (b) 2. (a) 3. (c) 4. (a) 5. (a) 6. (b)

Exercise 65 *page 52*

1. (b) 2. (c) 3. (b) 4. (d) 5. (c) 6. (a)

BOOK 1   PART 4

Exercise 66 *page 54*

1. Barrhead (0, 10)   Coatbridge (25, 15)
   Clydebank (0, 20)   Carron Bridge (25, 35)
   Aberfoyle (0, 50)   Airdrie (30, 15)
   Pollokshaws (5, 10)   Stirling (30, 45)
   Milngavie (5, 25)   Dunblane (30, 50)
   Balfron (5, 40)   Falkirk (40, 30)
   Glasgow (10, 15)   Alloa (40, 45)
   Fintry (10, 35)   Braehead (45, 0)
   East Kilbride (15, 5)   Bathgate (45, 20)
   Kirkintilloch (15, 25)   Linlithgow (50, 25)

2. Hereford (0, 10)
  Leominster (0, 30)
  Ludlow (0, 45)
  Tenbury Wells (10, 40)
  Cleedownton (10, 50)
  Bromyard (15, 25)
  Cleobury Mortimer (15, 45)
  Ledbury (20, 10)
  Stanford-on-Teme (20, 35)
  Great Malvern (25, 15)

  Great Witley (25, 35)
  Welland (30, 10)
  Stourport (30, 40)
  Worcester (35, 25)
  Kidderminster (35, 45)
  Tewkesbury (40, 5)
  Droitwich Spa (40, 35)
  Pershore (45, 15)
  Bromsgrove (45, 40)
  Winchcombe (50, 0)

3. Jane (1, 1)
  Wendy (1, 3)
  Peter (1, 4)
  John (2, 1)
  Anne (2, 2)

  Susan (2, 4)
  Julie (2, 5)
  David (3, 1)
  William (3, 2)
  Linda (3, 5)

  Jill (4, 3)
  Michael (4, 4)
  Janet (5, 1)
  Andrew (5, 3)
  Steven (5, 5)

4.

Exercise 67 *page 56*

A (0, 2), B (0, 5), C (1, 1), D (1, 7), E (2, 3), F (2, 8), G (3, 0)
H (3, 6), I (4, 4), J (4, 10), K (5, 2), L (5, 9), M (6, 0), N (6, 5)
P (7, 4), Q (7, 7), R (8, 1), S (8, 9), T (9, 3), U (9, 10), V (10, 6)
W (10, 8)

Exercise 68 *page 56*

1. ship   **2.** saucepan   **3.** lamp   **4.** aeroplane   **5.** spade
6. key   **7.** spanner   **8.** British Rail sign
9. coat hanger   **10.** traffic light

Exercise 69 *page 58*

A (1, 2),   B (1, 5),   C (1, −2),   D (1, −3),   E (2, 0)   F (2, 4),
G (2, −1),   H (2, −3),   I (4, 0),   J (4, 3),   K (4, −2),   L (4, −5),
M (−1, 0),   N (−1, 2),   P (−1, 3),   Q (−1, −2), R (−1, −5), S (−3, 1),
T (−3, 4),   U (−3, −1), V (−3, −3), W (−5, 0),   X (−5, 5),   Y (−5, −4),
Z (0, −4)

Exercise 70   *page 59*   1. cricket bat   2. christmas tree   3. rolling pin   4. arrow
5. compass and pencil   6. cup and saucer   7. tank
8. elephant   9. horse   10. windmill   11. flag

BOOK 1   PART 5

Exercise 72   *page 62*   1. 8 cm^2 2. 9 cm^2 3. 9 cm^2 4. 12 cm^2 5. 13 cm^2
6. 5 cm^2 7. 6 cm^2 8. 8 cm^2 9. 8 cm^2 10. 9 cm^2

Exercise 73   *page 63*   1. (c)   2. (b)   3. (b)   4. (a)   5. (c)
6. (a)   7. (a)   8. (b)   9. (c)   10. (c)

Exercise 74   *page 64*   1. 6 cm^2 2. 8 cm^2 3. 12 cm^2 4. 15 cm^2 5. 10 cm^2
6. 12 cm^2 7. 18 cm^2 8. 4 cm^2 9. 4 cm^2 10. 9 cm^2

Exercise 75   *page 66*   1. cube   2. cuboid   3. cylinder   4. cylinder   5. sphere
6. triangular prism   7. cone   8. cone
9. triangular prism   10. cylinder, cone

Exercise 76   *page 69*   1. cm^3 2. cm^3 3. m^3 4. mm^3 5. cm^3
6. m^3 7. m^3 8. cm^3 9. mm^3 10. m^3

Exercise 77   *page 69*   1. (b)   2. (a)   3. (b)   4. (c)   5. (b)   6. (a)   7. (c)   8. (b)

Revision exercise C
page 71   1. 32 cm^2 2. $64 \text{ cm}^2, 96 \text{ cm}^2$ 3. 49 cm^2
4. $10 \text{ cm}^2, 36 \text{ cm}^2$ 5. 18 cm^3 6. 36 cm^3

BOOK 1   PART 6

Exercise 78   *page 72*   1. {1, 3, 5, 7, 9}   2. {1, 4, 9}   3. {2, 3, 5, 7}   4. {3, 6, 9}
5. {4, 8}   6. {2, 4, 6, 8, 10}   7. {5, 10}   8. {1, 3, 6, 10}
9. { January, June, July }   10. { Saturday, Sunday }
11. { Spring, Summer, Autumn, Winter }
12. { days of week whose names begin with T }
13. { months of the year whose names begin with A }
14. { seasons of the year whose names begin with S }
15. { months with five-letter names }   16. { months with four-letter names }
17. { months with seven-letter names }   18. { days with six-letter names }
19. { days with eight-letter names }   20. { months with eight-letter names }

Exercise 79   *page 72*   1. (a) { 2, 4, 6}   (b) {1, 3, 5}   (c) {3, 6}
2. (a) { 3, 6, 9, 12}   (b) {4, 8, 12}   (c) { 6, 12}   (d) {1, 4, 9
3. (a) { 5, 10, 15, 20}   (b) { 6, 12, 18}   (c) {2, 3, 5, 7, 11, 13, 17, 19}
4. (a) { 2, 3, 5, 7}   (b) {4, 9}   (c) {3, 6, 10}
5. (a) { 2, 5}   (b) {5, 10, 50}
6. (a) { Atlantic, Arctic }   (b) { Indian, Arctic }

7. (a) { London, Dublin}   (b) { Cardiff, Belfast }
8. (a) { orange, blue }   (b) { red, blue}
9. (a) { 4, 16, 36}   (b) { 36}
10. (a) { 3, 6, 15, 21}   (b) { 10, 15}
11. { units of weight }   12. { units of volume}   13. { angles}
14. { points of the compass}   15. { continents }   16. { planets}
17. { crisps }   18.{pies}   19.{flowers}   20.{trees}

Exercise 80 *page 73*

1. (c)   2. (b)   3. (e)   4. (b)   5. (c)   6. (c)   7. (a), (c)
8. (a)   9. (b), (c)   10. (b), (c)

Exercise 81 *page 74*

1. (a) { 2, 4}   (b) {2, 4, 6, 8}   2. (a) {1, 3}   (b) {1, 2, 3, 5}
3. (a) {1}   (b) {1, 4, 8, 9, 27} 4. (a) {10}   (b) {5, 10, 15, 20, 30}
5. (a) {R, G, V}   (b) {R, O, Y, G, B, I, V}
6. (a) {ash, oak}   (b) {ash, oak, elm, alder }
7. (a) {June}   (b) {January, April, June, July, September, November}
8. (a) {P, A, T}   (b) {P, A, T, C, H}
9. (a) {2, 3, 4, 5, 6} (b) {1, 2, 3, 4, 5, 6, 7, 8, 9, 10}
10. (a) ϕ (b) {1, 2, 3, 4, 5, 6, 7, 8, 9, 10 }

Exercise 82 *page 74*

1. (a) {2} (b) {6}   (c) {3}   2. (a) {4} (b) {6}   (c) {1}
3. (a) {2} (b) {4}   (c) ϕ
4. (a) {3} (b) {1, 3, 6}   (c) {2, 3, 5}   (d) {3}
5. (a) {1} (b) {1, 3, 6}   (c) {1, 4}   (d) {1}
6. (a) ϕ (b) {2, 3, 5}   (c) {1, 4}   (d) ϕ
7. (a) ϕ (b) {3}   (c) ϕ (d) {1}
8. (a) {1, 3, 4, 5}   (b) {1, 3, 5, 6}   (c) {1, 3, 4, 6}   (d) {1, 3, 4, 5, 6}
9. (a) {1, 2, 3, 5}   (b) {1, 3, 5, 6}   (c) {1, 2, 3, 5, 6} (d) {1, 2, 3, 5, 6}
10. (a) {1, 3, 4, 5} (b) {1, 2, 3, 5 }   (c) {1, 2, 3, 4, 5} (d) {1, 2, 3, 4, 5}

Exercise 83 *page 76*

1. (a) $\binom{11}{9}, \binom{8}{7}, \binom{10}{8}, \binom{9}{7}, \binom{12}{9}$ (b) $\binom{50}{40}$ (c) $\binom{5}{4}$ (d) $\binom{3}{2}$

2. (a) $\begin{pmatrix} 1 \\ 2 \\ 2 \end{pmatrix}, \begin{pmatrix} 0 \\ 0 \\ 1 \end{pmatrix}, \begin{pmatrix} 0 \\ 1 \\ 1 \end{pmatrix}, \begin{pmatrix} 2 \\ 1 \\ 0 \end{pmatrix}$ (b) $\begin{pmatrix} 3 \\ 4 \\ 4 \end{pmatrix}$,   (c) $\begin{pmatrix} 1 \\ 2 \\ 1 \end{pmatrix}$

3. (a) $\begin{pmatrix} 2 \\ 1 \\ 2 \end{pmatrix}, \begin{pmatrix} 1 \\ 0 \\ 0 \end{pmatrix}, \begin{pmatrix} 1 \\ 0 \\ 1 \end{pmatrix}, \begin{pmatrix} 1 \\ 1 \\ 0 \end{pmatrix}$ (b) $\begin{pmatrix} 5 \\ 2 \\ 3 \end{pmatrix}$ (c) $\begin{pmatrix} 1 \\ 1 \\ 2 \end{pmatrix}, \begin{pmatrix} 1 \\ 1 \\ 1 \end{pmatrix}, \begin{pmatrix} 1 \\ 0 \\ 2 \end{pmatrix}$

4. (a) $\begin{pmatrix} 4 \\ 3 \\ 2 \\ 3 \end{pmatrix}, \begin{pmatrix} 3 \\ 1 \\ 1 \\ 2 \end{pmatrix}, \begin{pmatrix} 2 \\ 4 \\ 2 \\ 1 \end{pmatrix}, \begin{pmatrix} 1 \\ 7 \\ 3 \\ 0 \end{pmatrix}$ (b) $\begin{pmatrix} 10 \\ 15 \\ 8 \\ 6 \end{pmatrix}$, £1·40   (c) $\begin{pmatrix} 1 \\ 2 \\ 1 \\ 1 \end{pmatrix}$, 20 p

5. (a) $\begin{pmatrix} 4 \\ 6 \\ 6 \end{pmatrix}, \begin{pmatrix} 4 \\ 2 \\ 4 \end{pmatrix}, \begin{pmatrix} 5 \\ 3 \\ 1 \end{pmatrix}, \begin{pmatrix} 2 \\ 1 \\ 3 \end{pmatrix}$ (b) $\begin{pmatrix} 15 \\ 12 \\ 14 \end{pmatrix}$

6. (a) $\begin{pmatrix} 10 \\ 9 \\ 11 \\ 12 \\ 8 \end{pmatrix}, \begin{pmatrix} 5 \\ 7 \\ 7 \\ 6 \\ 5 \end{pmatrix}, \begin{pmatrix} 8 \\ 7 \\ 7 \\ 8 \\ 10 \end{pmatrix}, \begin{pmatrix} 6 \\ 8 \\ 11 \\ 6 \\ 9 \end{pmatrix}, \begin{pmatrix} 11 \\ 9 \\ 14 \\ 8 \\ 8 \end{pmatrix},$ (b) $\begin{pmatrix} 40 \\ 40 \\ 50 \\ 40 \\ 40 \end{pmatrix}$

7. (a) $\begin{pmatrix} 50 \\ 40 \\ 60 \end{pmatrix}, \begin{pmatrix} 30 \\ 25 \\ 40 \end{pmatrix}, \begin{pmatrix} 20 \\ 15 \\ 30 \end{pmatrix}, \begin{pmatrix} 25 \\ 30 \\ 35 \end{pmatrix}$ (b) $\begin{pmatrix} 125 \\ 110 \\ 165 \end{pmatrix}$, £60

8. (a) $\begin{pmatrix} 40 \\ 30 \\ 30 \end{pmatrix}, \begin{pmatrix} 30 \\ 15 \\ 25 \end{pmatrix}, \begin{pmatrix} 25 \\ 15 \\ 25 \end{pmatrix}, \begin{pmatrix} 15 \\ 20 \\ 30 \end{pmatrix}$ (b) $\begin{pmatrix} 110 \\ 80 \\ 110 \end{pmatrix}$, £75

9. (a) $\begin{pmatrix} 50 \\ 40 \\ 60 \\ 50 \\ 30 \end{pmatrix}, \begin{pmatrix} 20 \\ 15 \\ 15 \\ 10 \\ 5 \end{pmatrix}, \begin{pmatrix} 20 \\ 15 \\ 25 \\ 30 \\ 15 \end{pmatrix},$ (b) $\begin{pmatrix} 90 \\ 70 \\ 100 \\ 90 \\ 50 \end{pmatrix}$, £800

10. (a) $\begin{pmatrix} 4 \\ 6 \end{pmatrix}, \begin{pmatrix} 1 \\ 1 \end{pmatrix}, \begin{pmatrix} 0 \\ 2 \end{pmatrix}, \begin{pmatrix} 2 \\ 0 \end{pmatrix}, \begin{pmatrix} 1 \\ 1 \end{pmatrix}, \begin{pmatrix} 1 \\ 0 \end{pmatrix}$ (b) $\begin{pmatrix} 9 \\ 10 \end{pmatrix}$ (c) $\begin{pmatrix} 16 \\ 16 \end{pmatrix}$ (d) $\begin{pmatrix} 7 \\ 6 \end{pmatrix}$

Exercise 84   *page 79*

1. (a) (2 0 1 1), (1 1 2 0), (1 2 3 1)
(b) (4 3 6 2)
2. (a) (5 3 4 5), (1 4 1 3), (2 1 3 0)
(b) (6 7 5 8)
3. (a) (50 45 30 25), (35 40 20 45), (25 35 20 30)
(b) (110 120 70 100), £100
4. (a) (50 20 30 10 5), (40 15 20 5 10), (30 25 20 15
(b) (120 60 70 30 20), £150
5. (a) (10 20 15 10), (10 15 10 20), (5 10 15 15),
(10 10 15 15), (15 15 5 10), (10 20 10 10),
(b) (60 90 70 80), £60
6. (a) (3 3 0), (1 2 1), (2 4 0), (2 2 0)
(b) (8 11 1), yes

Exercise 85   *page 81*   **1.** $\begin{pmatrix} 10 \\ 5 \\ 15 \end{pmatrix}$ **2.** $\begin{pmatrix} 15 \\ 10 \\ 20 \end{pmatrix}$ **3.** $\begin{pmatrix} 20 \\ 10 \\ 5 \end{pmatrix}$ **4.** $\begin{pmatrix} 5 \\ 15 \\ 20 \end{pmatrix}$ **5.** $\begin{pmatrix} 15 \\ 10 \\ 15 \end{pmatrix}$ **6.** $\begin{pmatrix} 10 \\ 5 \\ 10 \end{pmatrix}$

7. $\begin{pmatrix} 15 \\ 10 \\ 5 \end{pmatrix}$ **8.** $\begin{pmatrix} 10 \\ 5 \\ 0 \end{pmatrix}$ **9.** $\begin{pmatrix} 5 \\ 0 \\ 15 \end{pmatrix}$ **10.** $\begin{pmatrix} 20 \\ 0 \\ 10 \end{pmatrix}$ **11.** $\begin{pmatrix} 15 \\ 10 \end{pmatrix}$ **12.** $\begin{pmatrix} 20 \\ 15 \end{pmatrix}$

13. $\begin{pmatrix} 25 \\ 10 \end{pmatrix}$ **14.** $\begin{pmatrix} 25 \\ 15 \end{pmatrix}$ **15.** $\begin{pmatrix} 20 \\ 10 \end{pmatrix}$ **16.** $\begin{pmatrix} 10 \\ 5 \end{pmatrix}$ **17.** $\begin{pmatrix} 15 \\ 10 \end{pmatrix}$ **18.** $\begin{pmatrix} 15 \\ 5 \end{pmatrix}$

19. $\begin{pmatrix} 10 \\ 15 \end{pmatrix}$ **20.** $\begin{pmatrix} 5 \\ 10 \end{pmatrix}$ **21.** $\begin{pmatrix} 20 \\ 10 \end{pmatrix}$ **22.** $\begin{pmatrix} 25 \\ 15 \end{pmatrix}$ **23.** $\begin{pmatrix} 30 \\ 20 \end{pmatrix}$ **24.** $\begin{pmatrix} 25 \\ 30 \end{pmatrix}$

25. $\begin{pmatrix} 20 \\ 30 \end{pmatrix}$ **26.** $\begin{pmatrix} 10 \\ 5 \end{pmatrix}$ **27.** $\begin{pmatrix} 15 \\ 10 \end{pmatrix}$ **28.** $\begin{pmatrix} 5 \\ 10 \end{pmatrix}$ **29.** $\begin{pmatrix} 10 \\ 15 \end{pmatrix}$ **30.** $\begin{pmatrix} 15 \\ 5 \end{pmatrix}$

answers

BOOK 2   PART 1

Exercise 1 *page 1*   **1.** (b)   **2.** (b)   **3.** (a)   **4.** (a)   **5.** (c)   **6.** (b)   **7.** (a)   **8.** (a)
9. (c)   **10.** (b)

Exercise 2 *page 1*   **1.** (c)   **2.** (b)   **3.** (c)   **4.** (a)   **5.** (a)   **6.** (c)   **7.** (a)   **8.** (b)
9. (a)   **10.** (a)   **11.** (a)   **12.** (b)   **13.** (b)   **14.** (c)   **15.** (a)

Exercise 3 *page 1*   **1.** 720   **2.** 650   **3.** 840   **4.** 1120   **5.** 1920
6. 4050   **7.** 8640   **8.** 8470   **9.** 8520   **10.** 7800
11. 2700   **12.** 4800   **13.** 8000   **14.** 35 000   **15.** 5600
16. 9600   **17.** 22 800   **18.** 29 600   **19.** 92 800   **20.** 68 000
21. 72 800   **22.** 84 000   **23.** 72 000   **24.** 96 000

Exercise 4 *page 1*   **1.** 585   **2.** 384   **3.** 576   **4.** 646   **5.** 855
6. 406   **7.** 768   **8.** 1092   **9.** 1848   **10.** 1625
11. (b)   **12.** (b)   **13.** (a)   **14.** (a)   **15.** (c)
16. (b)   **17.** (a)   **18.** (b)   **19.** (b)   **20.** (c)

Exercise 5 *page 2*   **1.** 72 cm   **2.** 96 km, 128 km   **3.** 948 m   **4.** 90 m
5. 84   **6.** 104   **7.** 120   **8.** 105, 630
9. 390 t   **10.** 325 m

Exercise 6 *page 3*   **1.** (b)   **2.** (a)   **3.** (d)   **4.** (a)   **5.** (c)   **6.** (d)
7. (b)   **8.** (b)   **9.** (c)   **10.** (a)   **11.** (d)   **12.** (c)

Exercise 7 *page 3*   **1.** (c)   **2.** (d)   **3.** (b)   **4.** (d)   **5.** (b)   **6.** (a)
7. (a)   **8.** (b)   **9.** (a)   **10.** (c)   **11.** (b)   **12.** (b)
13. (a)   **14.** (c)   **15.** (b)

Exercise 8 *page 4*   **1.** 15   **2.** 13   **3.** 12   **4.** 24   **5.** 23   **6.** 32
7. 31   **8.** 30   **9.** 45   **10.** 42   **11.** 54   **12.** 63
13. (a)   **14.** (c)   **15.** (b)   **16.** (b)   **17.** (c)   **18.** (a)
19. (c)   **20.** (b)   **21.** (a)   **22.** (b)   **23.** (a)   **24.** (c)
25. 13 r 3   **26.** 15 r 10   **27.** 14 r 10
28. 13 r 9   **29.** 11 r 8   **30.** 12 r 6

Exercise 9 *page 4*   **1.** 155 m*l*   **2.** 66   **3.** 19 weeks   **4.** 13
5. 64   **6.** 19 cm   **7.** 119 km   **8.** 45 kg
9. 35 g   **10.** 48   **11.** 78   **12.** 14 km
13. 5 cm   **14.** 16, 40 m*l*   **15.** 16, 12 t

Exercise 10 *page 6*   **1.** 170   **2.** 70   **3.** 130   **4.** 120   **5.** 300   **6.** 300, £60

Exercise 11 *page 8*

1.

8	6		6	2		2
	5	2		3	7	5
2		4	6			5
5	3		9	4		4
4	2	5		3	3	6
		8	2		4	
6	3	7		5	5	6

2.

3	4		5	3		9
	7	6		6	5	2
4		6	8			5
4	5		3	9		8
2	5	3		3	4	7
		8	7		5	
4	2	9		5	8	4

3.

7	2		8	4		3
	7	5		8	5	2
1		9	8			6
9	2		8	7		6
8	8	2		6	2	0
		9	0		3	
9	3	6		7	6	8

4.

1	9		3	8		8
	9	7		4	7	5
8		6	9			8
8	9		5	9		9
2	6	9		1	9	2
		4	5		7	
1	9	2		1	2	3

5.

1	6		1	5		2
	4	9		3	6	5
1		1	4			1
2	1		1	1		6
1	2	1		1	1	0
		1	0		0	
1	1	2		1	0	0

Exercise 12 *page 9*

1. 2, 4, 6, 8   **2.** 5, 10, 15, 20   **3.** 3, 6, 9, 12
4. 6, 12, 18, 24   **5.** 10, 20, 30, 40   **6.** 7, 14, 21, 28
7. 9, 18, 27, 36   **8.** 11, 22, 33, 44   **9.** 12, 24, 36, 48
10. 20, 40, 60, 80   **11.** 50, 100, 150, 200   **12.** 40, 80, 120, 160
13. 60, 120, 180, 240   **14.** 25, 50, 75, 100   **15.** 15, 30, 45, 60

Exercise 13 *page 9*

1. 13   **2.** 40   **3.** 62   **4.** 38   **5.** 74   **6.** 112   **7.** 34   **8.** 150
9. 70   **10.** 185

Exercise 14 *page 9*

1. 12   **2.** 30   **3.** 90   **4.** 20   **5.** 40   **6.** 15   **7.** 8   **8.** 12
9. 6   **10.** 10   **11.** 12   **12.** 30   **13.** 12   **14.** 24   **15.** 18   **16.** 36
17. 45   **18.** 30   **19.** 24   **20.** 60   **21.** 30   **22.** 36   **23.** 12   **24.** 20
25. 30

Exercise 15 *page 10*

1. 1, 2, 3, 6, 9, 18   **2.** 1, 2, 4, 5, 10, 20   **3.** 1, 2, 3, 4, 6, 12
4. 1, 2, 5, 10   **5.** 1, 2, 4, 8   **6.** 1, 2, 7, 14
7. 1, 2, 11, 22   **8.** 1, 3, 5, 15   **9.** 1, 3, 7, 21
10. 1, 3, 9, 27   **11.** 1, 5, 7, 35   **12.** 1, 2, 13, 26
13. 1, 2, 4, 7, 14, 28   **14.** 1, 2, 4, 8, 16, 32   **15.** 1, 2, 3, 5, 6, 10, 15, 30
16. 1, 2, 4, 5, 8, 10, 20, 40   **17.** 1, 2, 3, 4, 6, 9, 12, 18, 36
18. 1, 3, 9   **19.** 1, 5, 25   **20.** 1, 2, 4, 8, 16

Exercise 16 *page 10*

1. 8   **2.** 12   **3.** 9   **4.** 6   **5.** 12   **6.** 8   **7.** 6   **8.** 12
9. 6   **10.** 8   **11.** 9   **12.** 16   **13.** 15   **14.** 20   **15.** 16   **16.** 18
17. 14   **18.** 15   **19.** 24   **20.** 21   **21.** 6   **22.** 9   **23.** 8   **24.** 18
25. 15

Exercise 17 *page 11*

1. 2 × 3 × 5   **2.** 2 × 3 × 11   **3.** 2 × 5 × 7
4. 2 × 3 × 13   **5.** 2 × 5 × 11   **6.** 2 × 5 × 13
7. 2 × 7 × 11   **8.** 2 × 3 × 5 × 7   **9.** 2 × 2 × 3 × 7
10. 2 × 2 × 5 × 7   **11.** 2 × 2 × 3 × 11   **12.** 2 × 2 × 2 × 11
13. 2 × 2 × 2 × 13   **14.** 2 × 2 × 2 × 7   **15.** 2 × 2 × 2 × 5
16. 2 × 2 × 2 × 3 × 5   **17.** 2 × 2 × 2 × 3 × 3   **18.** 2 × 2 × 2 × 3 × 7

19. 2 × 2 × 2 × 2 × 5   20. 2 × 2 × 2 × 2 × 3   21. 2 × 2 × 2 × 2 × 7
22. 2 × 2 × 3 × 3 × 5   23. 2 × 2 × 3 × 3 × 3   24. 2 × 3 × 3 × 3 × 3

Exercise 18   *page 11*

1. (b)   2. (b)   3. (a)   4. (b)   5. (c)   6. (c)   7. (a)   8. (c)
9. (b)   10. (c)

Exercise 19   *page 12*

1. 6 cm   2. 8 cm   3. 10 cm   4. 5 cm, 50 mm
5. 35 mm   6. 45 mm   7. 25 mm   8. 5 m, 3 m, 8 m
9. 14 m, 5 m, 9 m, 2 m, 1 m, 3 m   10. 12 km, 17 km, 29 km

Exercise 20   *page 14*

1. 70 mm   2. 160 mm   3. 280 mm   4. 400 mm
5. 19 cm   6. 93 cm   7. 6 cm   8. 70 cm
9. 800 cm   10. 4500 cm   11. 23 600 cm   12. 32 000 cm
13. 50 000 cm   14. 3000 cm   15. 72 m   16. 518 m
17. 650 m   18. 800 m   19. 40 m   20. 4000 m
21. 79 000 km   22. 137 000 m   23. 50 000 m   24. 290 000 m
25. 100 000 m   26. 42 km   27. 215 km   28. 80 km
29. 460 km   30. 300 km   31. 2 m 15 cm   32. 6 m 32 cm
33. 3 m 4 cm   34. 1 km 595 m 35. 4 km 326 m 36. 2 km 350 m
37. 3 km 400 m 38. 5 km 76 m   39. 5 cm 4 mm   40. 7 cm 9 mm
41. 86 mm   42. 98 mm   43. 145 cm   44. 372 cm
45. 507 cm   46. 1870 m   47. 2356 m   48. 3058 m
49. 4080 m   50. 1005 m

Exercise 21   *page 14*

1. 1 cm 9 mm   2. 1 cm 4 mm   3. 2 cm 3 mm   4. 1 m 29 cm
5. 1 m 46 cm   6. 1 m 18 cm   7. 1 km 268 m   8. 1 km 574 m
9. 1 km 142 m   10. 1 km 64 m   11. (b)   12. (a)
13. (a)   14. (c)   15. (d)   16. (a)
17. 6 cm 9 mm   18. 8 cm 2 mm   19. 9 cm 5 mm   20. 7 m 76 cm
21. 9 m 84 cm   22. 9 m 62 cm   23. 8 km 752 m 24. 9 km 284 m
25. 7 km 345 m 26. 4 km 56 m   27. (c)   28. (b)
29. (d)   30. (a)   31. (a)   32. (c)

Exercise 22   *page 15*

1. 4 mm   2. 3 mm   3. 1 cm 6 mm   4. 3 cm 2 mm
5. 44 cm   6. 28 cm   7. 3 m 65 cm   8. 3 m 60 cm
9. 4 m 96 cm   10. 250 m   11. 1 km 355 m 12. 3 km 174 m
13. 1 km 932 m 14. 3 km 960 m 15. 3 km 995 m 16. 6 km 75 m
17. (c)   18. (a)   19. (b)   20. (b)   21. (b)
22. (a)   23. (b)   24. (c)   25. (a)

Exercise 23   *page 16*

1. g   2. kg   3. g   4. t   5. g
6. kg   7. kg   8. t   9. g   10. kg

Exercise 24   *page 16*

1. 5 kg   2. 32 kg   3. 8000 g   4. 41 000 g
5. 7 t   6. 96 t   7. 9000 kg   8. 80 000 kg
9. 2 kg 520 g 10. 8 kg 75 g 11. 4 t 372 kg 12. 5 t 4 kg
13. 3450 g   14. 5032 g   15. 6321 kg   16. 2009 kg

Exercise 25   *page 17*

1. 4 m 10 cm, 5, 90 cm   2. 70 cm   3. 4 m 80 cm
4. 85 g   5. 2 t 300 kg

Revision exercise A
page 18

1. (a) 280 mm   (b) 28 cm   2. (a) 200 cm   (b) 2 m
3. (a) 400 cm   (b) 4 m   4. (a) 2000 m   (b) 2 km

5. (a) 3000 g   (b) 3 kg   6. (a) 8000 g   (b) 8 kg
7. Yes   8. (a) 125 g   (b) 8   9. 36 g   10. 5 g
11. (c)   12. (a)

BOOK 2   PART 2

Exercise 26   *page 19*

1. $\frac{7}{9}$ 2. $\frac{8}{9}$ 3. $\frac{4}{9}$ 4. $\frac{4}{5}$ 5. $\frac{6}{7}$ 6. $\frac{4}{7}$ 7. $\frac{5}{7}$ 8. $\frac{3}{5}$

9. $\frac{7}{11}$ 10. $\frac{10}{11}$ 11. $\frac{4}{5}$ 12. $\frac{2}{5}$ 13. $\frac{3}{5}$ 14. $\frac{3}{4}$ 15. $\frac{5}{6}$ 16. $\frac{5}{8}$

17. $\frac{2}{3}$ 18. $\frac{1}{3}$ 19. $\frac{2}{3}$ 20. $\frac{1}{2}$ 21. $1\frac{1}{9}$ 22. $1\frac{2}{9}$ 23. $1\frac{5}{9}$ 24. $1\frac{1}{9}$

25. $1\frac{2}{5}$ 26. $1\frac{1}{5}$ 27. $1\frac{3}{5}$ 28. $1\frac{1}{7}$ 29. $1\frac{3}{7}$ 30. $1\frac{2}{7}$ 31. $1\frac{3}{5}$ 32. $1\frac{2}{5}$

33. 1 34. $1\frac{1}{4}$ 35. 1 36. $1\frac{3}{4}$ 37. 1 38. $1\frac{1}{3}$ 39. $1\frac{2}{3}$ 40. 1

41. 1 42. $1\frac{1}{5}$ 43. 1 44. 1 45. $1\frac{1}{2}$ 46. $1\frac{1}{4}$ 47. 1 48. 1

49. $1\frac{1}{3}$ 50. $1\frac{1}{2}$

Exercise 27   *page 19*

1. $\frac{2}{9}$ 2. $\frac{7}{9}$ 3. $\frac{4}{9}$ 4. $\frac{1}{9}$ 5. $\frac{5}{9}$ 6. $\frac{4}{9}$ 7. $\frac{2}{9}$ 8. $\frac{2}{5}$

9. $\frac{1}{5}$ 10. $\frac{2}{7}$ 11. $\frac{3}{7}$ 12. $\frac{4}{7}$ 13. $\frac{3}{7}$ 14. $\frac{7}{15}$ 15. $\frac{3}{5}$ 16. $\frac{2}{5}$

17. $\frac{1}{5}$ 18. $\frac{5}{6}$ 19. $\frac{1}{6}$ 20. $\frac{1}{4}$ 21. $\frac{3}{4}$ 22. $\frac{2}{3}$ 23. $\frac{1}{3}$ 24. $\frac{3}{5}$

25. $\frac{1}{5}$ 26. $\frac{1}{2}$ 27. $\frac{1}{3}$ 28. $\frac{2}{3}$ 29. $\frac{1}{3}$ 30. $\frac{1}{2}$

Exercise 28   *page 20*

1. $\frac{2}{3}$ 2. $\frac{2}{3}$ 3. $\frac{5}{12}$ 4. $\frac{1}{4}$ 5. $\frac{7}{9}$ 6. $\frac{4}{9}$ 7. $\frac{7}{12}$ 8. $\frac{2}{5}$

9. $\frac{5}{12}$ 10. $\frac{3}{5}$ 11. $\frac{3}{10}$ 12. $\frac{3}{8}$ 13. $\frac{4}{15}$ 14. $\frac{3}{20}$ 15. $\frac{11}{20}$

16. $\frac{7}{20}, \frac{1}{3}, \frac{3}{10}$ 17. $\frac{3}{4}, \frac{11}{15}, \frac{7}{10}$ 18. $\frac{7}{15}, \frac{9}{20}, \frac{5}{12}$ 19. $\frac{13}{15}, \frac{17}{20}, \frac{5}{6}$

20. $\frac{13}{20}, \frac{5}{8}, \frac{3}{5}$ 21. $\frac{2}{5}, \frac{3}{8}, \frac{7}{20}$

Exercise 29   *page 20*

1. $\frac{5}{12}$ 2. $\frac{7}{8}$ 3. $\frac{2}{3}$ 4. $\frac{5}{6}$ 5. $\frac{2}{5}$ 6. $\frac{1}{2}$ 7. $\frac{1}{3}$ 8. $\frac{7}{12}$

9. $\frac{7}{20}$ 10. $\frac{1}{15}$

Exercise 30   *page 21*

1. $\frac{7}{10}$ 2. $\frac{8}{15}$ 3. $\frac{7}{12}$ 4. $\frac{9}{20}$ 5. $\frac{3}{10}$ 6. $\frac{3}{8}$ 7. $\frac{5}{12}$ 8. $\frac{5}{8}$

9. $\frac{7}{20}$ 10. $\frac{5}{18}$ 11. $\frac{5}{12}$ 12. $\frac{7}{24}$ 13. $\frac{1}{2}$ 14. $\frac{2}{3}$ 15. $\frac{1}{3}$ 16. $\frac{1}{4}$

17. $\frac{11}{12}$ 18. $\frac{9}{10}$ 19. $\frac{7}{10}$ 20. $\frac{19}{20}$ 21. $\frac{1}{3}$ 22. $\frac{1}{2}$ 23. $\frac{9}{10}$ 24. $\frac{5}{6}$

25. $1\frac{1}{12}$ 26. $1\frac{2}{15}$ 27. $1\frac{7}{12}$ 28. $1\frac{1}{3}$ 29. $1\frac{1}{2}$ 30. $1\frac{1}{2}$ 31. $\frac{1}{2}$ 32. $\frac{1}{2}$

33. $\frac{1}{4}$ 34. $\frac{3}{10}$ 35. $\frac{1}{12}$ 36. $\frac{3}{20}$ 37. $\frac{1}{5}$ 38. $\frac{1}{3}$ 39. $\frac{1}{6}$ 40. $\frac{3}{10}$

41. $\frac{7}{12}$ 42. $\frac{4}{5}$ 43. $\frac{5}{6}$ 44. $\frac{9}{10}$ 45. $\frac{7}{8}$ 46. $\frac{1}{3}$ 47. $\frac{3}{5}$ 48. $\frac{1}{2}$

49. $\frac{1}{4}$ 50. $\frac{2}{5}$

Exercise 31　*page 21*　　**1.** $\frac{5}{6}$ m　**2.** $\frac{1}{3}$ m　**3.** $\frac{1}{15}$ m　**4.** yes, $\frac{1}{40}$ m is left.　**5.** $\frac{3}{5}$ litre

Exercise 32　*page 22*　　**1.** $1\frac{1}{2}$　**2.** $3\frac{1}{2}$　**3.** $1\frac{1}{3}$　**4.** $1\frac{2}{3}$　**5.** $2\frac{1}{3}$　**6.** $3\frac{2}{3}$　**7.** $4\frac{1}{3}$　**8.** $1\frac{1}{4}$

9. $1\frac{3}{4}$　**10.** $2\frac{1}{4}$　**11.** $3\frac{1}{4}$　**12.** $3\frac{3}{4}$　**13.** $4\frac{3}{4}$　**14.** $1\frac{1}{5}$　**15.** $1\frac{3}{5}$　**16.** $2\frac{1}{5}$

17. $2\frac{4}{5}$　**18.** $3\frac{2}{5}$　**19.** $3\frac{4}{5}$　**20.** $4\frac{1}{5}$

Exercise 33　*page 22*　　**1.** $\frac{1}{8}$　**2.** $\frac{1}{12}$　**3.** $\frac{1}{12}$　**4.** $\frac{1}{30}$　**5.** $\frac{1}{20}$　**6.** $\frac{1}{16}$　**7.** $\frac{1}{40}$　**8.** $\frac{1}{30}$

9. $\frac{1}{40}$　**10.** $\frac{1}{50}$　**11.** $\frac{3}{10}$　**12.** $\frac{5}{12}$　**13.** $\frac{3}{20}$　**14.** $\frac{7}{20}$　**15.** $\frac{2}{15}$　**16.** $\frac{2}{9}$

17. $\frac{4}{15}$　**18.** $\frac{3}{20}$　**19.** $\frac{9}{40}$　**20.** $\frac{3}{50}$　**21.** $\frac{1}{5}$　**22.** $\frac{2}{5}$　**23.** $\frac{4}{9}$　**24.** $\frac{1}{4}$

25. $\frac{1}{6}$　**26.** $\frac{1}{8}$　**27.** $\frac{1}{9}$　**28.** $\frac{2}{15}$　**29.** $\frac{1}{10}$　**30.** $\frac{3}{40}$　**31.** $\frac{3}{10}$　**32.** $\frac{5}{8}$

33. $\frac{7}{10}$　**34.** $\frac{4}{15}$　**35.** $\frac{6}{25}$　**36.** $\frac{1}{12}$　**37.** $\frac{1}{8}$　**38.** $\frac{1}{6}$　**39.** $\frac{2}{3}$　**40.** $\frac{3}{8}$

Exercise 34　*page 23*　　**1.** $1\frac{1}{2}$　**2.** $1\frac{1}{3}$　**3.** $1\frac{1}{5}$　**4.** $1\frac{1}{9}$　**5.** $1\frac{3}{5}$　**6.** $2\frac{2}{3}$　**7.** $3\frac{1}{3}$　**8.** $2\frac{2}{5}$

9. 3　**10.** 6　**11.** $\frac{1}{5}$　**12.** $\frac{1}{7}$　**13.** $\frac{1}{8}$　**14.** $\frac{1}{2}$　**15.** $\frac{1}{9}$　**16.** $\frac{1}{10}$

17. $\frac{1}{12}$　**18.** $\frac{1}{15}$　**19.** $\frac{1}{20}$　**20.** $\frac{1}{25}$　**21.** $\frac{4}{5}$　**22.** $\frac{8}{9}$　**23.** $\frac{3}{5}$　**24.** $\frac{4}{7}$

25. $\frac{5}{9}$　**26.** $\frac{4}{9}$　**27.** $\frac{3}{10}$　**28.** $\frac{2}{9}$　**29.** $\frac{4}{15}$　**30.** $\frac{6}{25}$

Exercise 35　*page 23*　　**1.** $1\frac{1}{2}$　**2.** $2\frac{1}{2}$　**3.** 2　**4.** $\frac{2}{3}$　**5.** $1\frac{2}{3}$　**6.** 1　**7.** $2\frac{2}{3}$　**8.** 4

9. $\frac{3}{4}$　**10.** $1\frac{1}{4}$　**11.** 1　**12.** $1\frac{1}{2}$　**13.** $2\frac{1}{2}$　**14.** 3　**15.** 6　**16.** 12

17. 8　**18.** 15　**19.** 16　**20.** $\frac{5}{6}$　**21.** $\frac{5}{8}$　**22.** $\frac{4}{9}$　**23.** $\frac{9}{20}$　**24.** $1\frac{1}{4}$

25. $1\frac{1}{8}$　**26.** $1\frac{1}{6}$　**27.** 1　**28.** $\frac{2}{3}$　**29.** $\frac{4}{5}$　**30.** $\frac{2}{5}$　**31.** $\frac{2}{3}$　**32.** $\frac{3}{8}$

33. $\frac{3}{10}$　**34.** $\frac{5}{12}$　**35.** $\frac{5}{14}$　**36.** $1\frac{1}{3}$　**37.** $1\frac{2}{3}$　**38.** $1\frac{1}{2}$　**39.** $4\frac{1}{2}$　**40.** $7\frac{1}{2}$

41. $7\frac{1}{2}$　**42.** $\frac{3}{4}$　**43.** $\frac{2}{3}$　**44.** $\frac{3}{4}$　**45.** $\frac{2}{3}$　**46.** $\frac{3}{10}$　**47.** $1\frac{1}{3}$　**48.** 6

49. $1\frac{1}{2}$　**50.** $1\frac{1}{5}$

Exercise 36　*page 24*　　**1.** (a) 150 g　(b) 225 g　(c) 48 g　　**2.** (a) 60　(b) 144

3. (a) 600 m　(b) 625 m　　**4.** 5　　**5.** 15

Exercise 37　*page 25*　　**1.** 1·4　**2.** 3·2　**3.** 5·4　**4.** 6·3　**5.** 3

6. 4·8　**7.** 5·5　**8.** 4·8　**9.** 8·4　**10.** 12·8

11. 11·5　**12.** 25·6　**13.** 1·35　**14.** 1·68　**15.** 2·82

16. 3·78　**17.** 2·1　**18.** 2　**19.** 1·692　**20.** 0·8

21. 0·72　**22.** 0·8　**23.** 0·768　**24.** 0·48　**25.** 0·63

26. 0·4　**27.** 0·08　**28.** 0·06　**29.** 0·09　**30.** 0·12

31. 0·24　**32.** 0·42　**33.** 0·3　**34.** 0·1　**35.** 0·096

36. 0·072　**37.** 0·09　**38.** 0·192　**39.** 0·165　**40.** 0·008

41. 0·006　**42.** 0·015　**43.** 0·048　**44.** 0·84　**45.** 0·66

46. 0·65　**47.** 0·64　**48.** 0·91　**49.** 1·35　**50.** 1·38

51. 2·56　**52.** 1·92　**53.** 1·8　**54.** 0·372　**55.** 0·384

56. 0·624　**57.** 0·66　**58.** 1·312　**59.** 1·736　**60.** 1·092

Exercise 38　*page 25*　　**1.** 3·22　**2.** 5·12　**3.** 6·45　**4.** 3·78　**5.** 4·68

6. 5·25	**7.** 3·6	**8.** 8·4	**9.** 13·12	**10.** 11·76
11. 13·95	**12.** 12·72	**13.** 10·08	**14.** 13·2	**15.** 16
16. 0·448	**17.** 0·585	**18.** 0·432	**19.** 0·756	**20.** 0·588
21. 0·864	**22.** 0·696	**23.** 0·72	**24.** 1·472	**25.** 1·204
26. 1·512	**27.** 1·066	**28.** 1·012	**29.** 1·26	**30.** 1·4

Exercise 39 *page 26*

1. 3·4	**2.** 3·8	**3.** 2·9	**4.** 2·6	**5.** 3·4	**6.** 4·4
7. 5·3	**8.** 4·5	**9.** 1·6	**10.** 1·7	**11.** 1·3	**12.** 2·9
13. 2·4	**14.** 0·9	**15.** 0·5	**16.** 0·8	**17.** 0·7	**18.** 0·6
19. 0·8	**20.** 0·9	**21.** 0·6	**22.** 0·5	**23.** 1·5	**24.** 1·6
25. 3·5	**26.** 2·5	**27.** 3·4	**28.** 4·5	**29.** 10·5	**30.** 11·2

Exercise 40 *page 26*

1. 17·6	**2.** 14·5	**3.** 12·2	**4.** 10·6	**5.** 16·1	**6.** 18
7. 26	**8.** 14·5	**9.** 19·2	**10.** 6·7	**11.** 8·6	**12.** 7·2
13. 8·6	**14.** 1·3	**15.** 1·4	**16.** 1·8	**17.** 1·5	**18.** 17
19. 38	**20.** 34	**21.** 28	**22.** 35	**23.** 34	**24.** 20
25. 1·3	**26.** 1·2	**27.** 1·9	**28.** 0·8	**29.** 0·7	**30.** 0·9

Exercise 41 *page 27*

1. £27	**2.** 3 kg	**3.** 9 m, £10·80	**4.** 9·6 cm	**5.** 15	**6.** 25
7. 6	**8.** 0·9 kg				

Exercise 42 *page 28*

1. 0·2	**2.** 0·6	**3.** 0·1	**4.** 0·9	**5.** 0·18
6. 0·26	**7.** 0·42	**8.** 0·54	**9.** 0·62	**10.** 0·86
11. 0·78	**12.** 0·02	**13.** 0·15	**14.** 0·35	**15.** 0·65
16. 0·95	**17.** 0·05	**18.** 0·16	**19.** 0·24	**20.** 0·36
21. 0·48	**22.** 0·72	**23.** 0·08	**24.** 0·75	**25.** 0·122
26. 0·106	**27.** 0·105	**28.** 0·408	**29.** 0·125	**30.** 0·875

Exercise 43 *page 28*

1. $\frac{3}{10}$	**2.** $\frac{19}{100}$	**3.** $\frac{27}{100}$	**4.** $\frac{81}{100}$	**5.** $\frac{99}{100}$	**6.** $\frac{3}{100}$
7. $\frac{7}{100}$	**8.** $\frac{1}{100}$	**9.** $\frac{123}{1000}$	**10.** $\frac{361}{1000}$	**11.** $\frac{729}{1000}$	**12.** $\frac{887}{1000}$
13. $\frac{13}{1000}$	**14.** $\frac{61}{1000}$	**15.** $\frac{11}{1000}$	**16.** $\frac{39}{1000}$	**17.** $\frac{87}{1000}$	**18.** $\frac{9}{1000}$
19. $\frac{7}{1000}$	**20.** $\frac{1}{1000}$				

Exercise 44 *page 29*

1. $\frac{4}{5}$	**2.** $\frac{9}{20}$	**3.** $\frac{11}{20}$	**4.** $\frac{17}{20}$	**5.** $\frac{7}{50}$	**6.** $\frac{11}{50}$
7. $\frac{23}{50}$	**8.** $\frac{41}{50}$	**9.** $\frac{19}{50}$	**10.** $\frac{49}{50}$	**11.** $\frac{8}{25}$	**12.** $\frac{3}{25}$
13. $\frac{11}{25}$	**14.** $\frac{16}{25}$	**15.** $\frac{18}{25}$	**16.** $\frac{14}{25}$	**17.** $\frac{7}{40}$	**18.** $\frac{9}{40}$
19. $\frac{19}{40}$	**20.** $\frac{11}{40}$	**21.** $\frac{3}{40}$	**22.** $\frac{1}{40}$	**23.** $\frac{3}{250}$	**24.** $\frac{2}{125}$
25. $\frac{11}{125}$	**26.** $\frac{3}{500}$	**27.** $\frac{1}{125}$	**28.** $\frac{1}{200}$	**29.** $\frac{1}{500}$	**30.** $\frac{1}{250}$

Exercise 45 *page 29*

1. $\frac{4}{5}$, 0·8	**2.** $1\frac{2}{5}$, 1·4	**3.** $\frac{7}{10}$, 0·7	**4.** $\frac{2}{5}$, 0·4	**5.** $1\frac{1}{10}$, 1·1	**6.** $\frac{1}{5}$, 0·2
7. $\frac{1}{5}$, 0·2	**8.** $\frac{3}{5}$, 0·6	**9.** $\frac{1}{5}$, 0·2	**10.** $\frac{3}{10}$, 0·3	**11.** (c)	**12.** (b)
13. (b)	**14.** (c)	**15.** (c)	**16.** (a)	**17.** (b)	**18.** (c)
19. (a)	**20.** (b)	**21.** (a)	**22.** (c)	**23.** (b)	**24.** (a)
25. (a)	**26.** (c)				

Exercise 46 *page 30*

1. 4:5	**2.** 5:6	**3.** 3:8	**4.** 5:8	**5.** 1:2	**6.** 3:4
7. 4:5	**8.** 5:8	**9.** 9:10	**10.** 1:3	**11.** 2:3	**12.** 4:5

13. 9:10	**14.** 2:3	**15.** 3:4	**16.** 2:5	**17.** 5:8	**18.** 1:5
19. 3:5	**20.** 5:6	**21.** 5:8	**22.** 3:5	**23.** 7:8	**24.** 2:3
25. 4:5	**26.** 3:4	**27.** 3:5	**28.** 2:5	**29.** 5:8	**30.** 1:5
31. 1:4	**32.** 1:6	**33.** 2:5	**34.** 3:10	**35.** 1:4	**36.** 4:5
37. 4:5	**38.** 3:4	**39.** 3:5	**40.** 3:8	**41.** 1:2	**42.** 3:10
43. 1:6	**44.** 9:10	**45.** 4:5	**46.** 3:4	**47.** 5:6	**48.** 1:4
49. 1:8	**50.** 1:5				

Exercise 47 *page 30*

1. 2:3	**2.** 7:10	**3.** 4:5	**4.** 3:4	**5.** 3:5	**6.** 4:5
7. 2:3	**8.** 1:3	**9.** 1:4	**10.** 3:4		

Exercise 48 *page 31*

1. $\frac{63}{100}$	**2.** $\frac{29}{100}$	**3.** $\frac{13}{100}$	**4.** $\frac{43}{100}$	**5.** $\frac{77}{100}$	**6.** $\frac{9}{100}$
7. $\frac{11}{50}$	**8.** $\frac{23}{50}$	**9.** $\frac{41}{50}$	**10.** $\frac{7}{50}$	**11.** $\frac{17}{50}$	**12.** $\frac{49}{50}$
13. $\frac{29}{50}$	**14.** $\frac{11}{20}$	**15.** $\frac{17}{20}$	**16.** $\frac{3}{20}$	**17.** $\frac{1}{20}$	**18.** $\frac{12}{25}$
19. $\frac{16}{25}$	**20.** $\frac{18}{25}$	**21.** $\frac{21}{25}$	**22.** $\frac{9}{25}$	**23.** $\frac{7}{25}$	**24.** $\frac{3}{25}$
25. $\frac{2}{25}$	**26.** $\frac{3}{10}$	**27.** $\frac{1}{10}$	**28.** $\frac{3}{5}$	**29.** $\frac{2}{5}$	**30.** $\frac{1}{4}$

Exercise 49 *page 31*

1. $\frac{1}{40}$	**2.** $\frac{7}{40}$	**3.** $\frac{9}{40}$	**4.** $\frac{13}{40}$	**5.** $\frac{21}{40}$	**6.** $\frac{11}{40}$
7. $\frac{1}{12}$	**8.** $\frac{1}{30}$	**9.** $\frac{7}{30}$	**10.** $\frac{11}{60}$	**11.** $\frac{1}{6}$	**12.** $\frac{7}{60}$
13. $\frac{13}{60}$	**14.** $\frac{5}{12}$	**15.** $\frac{1}{16}$	**16.** $\frac{1}{80}$	**17.** $\frac{9}{80}$	**18.** $\frac{17}{80}$
19. $\frac{5}{16}$	**20.** $\frac{9}{16}$	**21.** $\frac{7}{80}$	**22.** $\frac{11}{80}$	**23.** $\frac{3}{16}$	**24.** $\frac{1}{24}$
25. $\frac{5}{24}$	**26.** $\frac{1}{75}$	**27.** $\frac{1}{32}$	**28.** $\frac{3}{32}$	**29.** $\frac{1}{14}$	**30.** $\frac{1}{9}$

Exercise 50 *page 32*

1. 31%	**2.** 27%	**3.** 87%	**4.** 99%	**5.** 3%	**6.** 1%
7. 18%	**8.** 42%	**9.** 38%	**10.** 54%	**11.** 45%	**12.** 65%
13. 95%	**14.** 16%	**15.** 24%	**16.** 4%	**17.** 32%	**18.** 44%
19. 52%	**20.** 56%	**21.** 68%	**22.** 70%	**23.** 80%	**24.** 75%
25. 50%					

Exercise 51 *page 32*

1. $62\frac{1}{2}\%$	**2.** $87\frac{1}{2}\%$	**3.** $83\frac{1}{3}\%$	**4.** $22\frac{2}{9}\%$	**5.** $7\frac{1}{2}\%$	**6.** $42\frac{1}{2}\%$
7. $72\frac{1}{2}\%$	**8.** $47\frac{1}{2}\%$	**9.** $16\frac{1}{4}\%$	**10.** $26\frac{1}{4}\%$	**11.** $41\frac{1}{4}\%$	**12.** $23\frac{3}{4}\%$
13. $33\frac{3}{4}\%$	**14.** $63\frac{1}{3}\%$	**15.** $36\frac{2}{3}\%$	**16.** $28\frac{1}{3}\%$	**17.** $48\frac{1}{3}\%$	**18.** $1\frac{2}{3}\%$
19. $31\frac{2}{3}\%$	**20.** $58\frac{1}{3}\%$	**21.** $91\frac{2}{3}\%$	**22.** $13\frac{1}{3}\%$	**23.** $53\frac{1}{3}\%$	**24.** $6\frac{2}{3}\%$
25. $26\frac{2}{3}\%$					

Revision exercise B
page 33

1. 20 km   **2.** (a) $1\frac{1}{5}$ m,   (b) 1·2 m   **3.** (a) $\frac{3}{4}$ kg,   (b) 0·75 kg

4. (a) $\frac{1}{20}$ kg,   (b) 0·05 kg   **5.** (a) $\frac{7}{20}$ l,   (b) 0·35 l

6. (a) $3\frac{3}{5}$ km, $7\frac{1}{2}$ km, $9\frac{3}{5}$ km   (b) 3·6 km, **7·5 km**, 9·6 km

7. (a) 45 kg,   (b) 60 kg,   (c) 67·5 kg,   (d) **7·5 kg**
8. (a) £3·90,   (b) £9·75,   (c) £6·28,   (d) **£4·71**,   (e) £4
9. (a) £12,   (b) £15,   (c) £18,   (d) £13·50,   **(e) £16·50**   (f) £75
10. (a) 2:3,   (b) 40%,   (c) 60%
11. (a) 1:3,   (b) 25%,   (c) 75%

BOOK 2   PART 3

Exercice 52 *page 34*	**1.** 50°	**2.** 75°	**3.** 45°	**4.** 125°	**5.** 95°	**6.** 70°
	7. 80°	**8.** 110°	**9.** 70°	**10.** 20°		

Exercice 53 *page 34*	**1.** 60°	**2.** 120°	**3.** 120°	**4.** 110°	**5.** 70°	**6.** 60°

Exercice 54 *page 35*

1. 120°, 60°, 120°
2. 110°, 70°, 110°
3. 160°, 20°, 160°
4. 105°, 75°, 105°
5. 155°, 25°, 155°
6. 80°, 100°, 80°
7. 50°, 130°, 50°
8. 30°, 150°, 30°
9. 40°, 140°, 40°
10. 45°, 135°, 45°

Exercice 55 *page 36*

1. 80°, acute-angled
2. 50°, acute-angled
3. 70°, acute-angled
4. 20°, acute-angled
5. 60°, right-angled
6. 90°, right-angled
7. 90°, right-angled
8. 40°, obtuse-angled
9. 100°, obtuse-angled
10. 120°, obtuse-angled

Exercice 56 *page 37*

1. 60°, 120°
2. 50°, 130°
3. 90°, 90°
4. 100°, 80°
5. 110°, 70°
6. 80°, 100°
7. 120°, 60°
8. 60°, 120°, 60°, 120°
9. 40°, 140°, 40°, 140°
10. 130°, 50°, 130°, 50°
11. 70°, 80°
12. 50°, 70°
13. 60°, 100°
14. 100°, 50°
15. 90°, 50°
16. 110°, 70°, 90°
17. 50°, 130°, 20°
18. 80°, 40°
19. 50°, 50°
20. 110°, 40°
21. 90°, 60°
22. 100°, 80°, 30°
23. 40°, 140°, 20°
24. 110°, 70°, 20°

Exercice 59 *page 40*	**1.** (c)	**2.** (d)	**3.** (b)	**4.** (d)	**5.** (c)	**6.** (a)

Revision exercise C *page 43*

1. 60°	**2.** 45°	**3.** 70°	**4.** 35°	**5.** 50°	**6.** 120°
7. 72°	**8.** 80°	**9.** 70°	**10.** 54°	**11.** 50°	**12.** 65°
13. 20°	**14.** 55°		**15.** 68°		**16.** 35°

17. (a) 4 cm,   (c) yes   **18.** (a) 16 cm   (b) no

BOOK 2   PART 4

Exercice 61 *page 45*

1. (a) 10 cm, 50 cm, 65 cm, 95 cm   (b) 2 p.m. to 3 p.m., 20 cm
   (c) 8 a.m. to 9 a.m., 5 cm   (d) 1 p.m. to 2 p.m.
2. (a) 3000, 6500, 1500, 4500, 9000   (b) 2 p.m. to 2.30 p.m., 3000
3. (a) 8 km, 14 km, 6 km, 16 km,   (b) 10 a.m. to 10.30 a.m., 5 km
   (c) 12.30 p.m. to 1.30 p.m.
4. (a) 20 s, 90 s, 100 s, 80 s, 30 s, 10 s   (b) 200 m to 400 m, 30 s
   (c) 600 m to 800 m, 50 s
5. (a) 30 *l*, 20 *l*, 25 *l*, 15 *l*   (b) 200 km to 300 km, 15 *l*   (c) 55 *l*

6. (a) 40, 260, 340, 10, 110   (b) 3 p.m. to 4 p.m., 120
    (c) 10 a.m. to 11 a.m., 20   (d) £30

7. (a) 19 l, 8 l, 12 l, 13 l (b) 5 p.m. to 5.30 p.m., 6l, 30 cups
                                          (c) 28 l

8. (a) 260, 160, 40, 160, 110   (b) 5.30 p.m. to 6 p.m., 120
    (c) 460, £13·80

Exercise 62   *page 50*

1. (a) 1000,   (b) £150   2. (a) 600,   (b) £180
3. (a) 150,   (b) £30   4. (a) 200,   (b) £225
5. (a) 90,   (b) 6 h   11. (a) 80,   (b) £40
12. (a) 150,   (b) £24

Exercise 63   *page 54*

1. (a) 6·4,   (b) 1·8   2. (a) 1·2,   (b) 7·6
3. (a) 156°,   (b) 108°,   (c) 36°,   (d) 12°
4. (a) 84 p,   (b) 58 p,   (c) 46 p,   (d) 24 p
5. (a) 5,   (b) 1·2   6. (a) 5,   (b) 1·6
7. (a) 45 ,   (b) 20   (c) 15   8. (a) 32 cm,   (b) 16 cm
10. 4 and 2   11. $4\frac{1}{2}$ and $1\frac{1}{2}$, or 4·5 and 1·5

BOOK 2   PART 5

Exercise 64   *page 56*

1. cm^2 2. cm^2 3. m^2 4. m^2 5. km^2 6. mm^2
7. mm^2 8. m^2 9. cm^2 10. cm^2

Exercise 65   *page 57*

1. (c)   2. (a)   3. (a)   4. (b)   5. (b)   6. (b)   7. (c)

Exercise 66   *page 58*

1. (a)   2. (c)   3. (b)   4. (a)   5. (c)   6. (a)   7. (a)

Exercise 67   *page 58*

1. 36 cm^2, 26 cm   2. 56 cm^2, 30 cm   3. 54 cm^2, 30 cm
4. 35 cm^2, 24 cm   5. 72 cm^2, 36 cm   6. 96 cm^2, 40 cm
7. 1500 mm^2, 160 mm   8. 7200 mm^2, 340 mm   9. 0·9 m^2, 4·6 m
10. 1·8 m^2, 5·4 m   11. 6 cm, 28 cm   12. 3 cm, 24 cm
13. 5 cm, 34 cm   14. 40 mm, 180 mm   15. 4 mm, 58 mm
16. 9 cm, 28 cm   17. 7 cm, 26 cm   18. 12 cm, 38 cm
19. 15 m, 38 m   20. 25 m, 56 m   21. 2 cm, 12 cm^2
22. 4 cm, 28 cm^2 23. 6 cm, 60 cm^2 24. 20 mm, 800 mm^2
25. 5 mm, 75 mm^2 26. 6 cm, 24 cm^2 27. 8 cm, 24 cm^2
28. 10 cm, 90 cm^2 29. 5 m, 20 m^2 30. 8 m, 40 m^2

Exercise 68   *page 59*

1. 12 cm^2, 20 cm   2. 7 cm^2, 16 cm   3. 12 cm^2, 26 cm
4. 8 cm^2, 14 cm   5. 9 cm^2, 16 cm

Exercise 69   *page 60*

1. 20 cm^2 2. 18 cm^2 3. 16 cm^2 4. 18 cm^2
5. 30 cm^2 6. 25 cm^2 7. 24 cm^2 8. 35 cm^2
9. 22 cm^2 10. 30 cm^2 11. 36 cm^2 12. 45 mm^2
13. 125 mm^2 14. 1200 mm^2 15. 1200 mm^2 16. 1400 mm^2
17. 0·3 m^2 18. 0·3 m^2 19. 0·4 m^2 20. 5 m^2

Exercise 70 *page 61*   **1.** 24   **2.** 200   **3.** 450   **4.** 80   **5.** 60

Exercise 71 *page 62*   **1.** (b)   **2.** (c)   **3.** (a)   **4.** (b)   **5.** (a)
6. (c)   **7.** (a)   **8.** (a)   **9.** (b)   **10.** (a)

Exercise 72 *page 63*   **1.** 3 cm   **2.** 2 cm   **3.** 4 cm   **4.** 3 cm   **5.** 8 cm
6. 7 cm   **7.** 5 cm   **8.** 4 cm   **9.** 5 cm   **10.** 3 cm
11. 6 cm   **12.** 12 cm   **13.** 4 m   **14.** 3 m   **15.** 0·5 m

Exercise 73 *page 64*   **1.** 4 l **2.** 6 l **3.** 3 l **4.** 10 l **5.** 12 l
6. 7·5 l **7.** 4·5 l **8.** 1·5 l **9.** 6·3 l **10.** 2·4 l
11. 5000 l **12.** 8000 l **13.** 2000 l **14.** 14 000 l **15.** 10 000 l
16. 2500 l **17.** 4200 l **18.** 6250 l **19.** 1250 l **20.** 8750 l
21. 0·75 l **22.** 0·45 l **23.** 0·6 l **24.** 0·9 l **25.** 0·065 l
26. 0·045 l **27.** 0·015 l **28.** 0·02 l **29.** 0·08 l **30.** 0·01 l

Exercise 74 *page 64*   **1.** 8 l **2.** 12 l **3.** 30 l **4.** 12l **5.** 45 l
6. 60 000 l **7.** 12 000 l **8.** 18 000 l **9.** 16 000 l **10.** 30 000 l
11. 400 l **12.** 300 l **13.** 1200 l **14.** 1500 l **15.** 1800 l

Exercise 75 *page 64*   **1.** 80 l **2.** 30 l, 150   **3.** 96   **4.** 9

Revision exercise D   **1.** (a) 300 cm^3,   (b) 300 ml,   (c) 0·3 l **2.** 480 km   **3.** yes
page 65   **4.** (a) 2 m^3,   (b) 2000 l **5.** (a) 0·2 m^3,   (b) 200 l (c) 8
6. 50   **7.** 10   **8.** 30   **9.** 960 cm^2
10. (a) 16 cm^2, 16 cm   (b) 19·6 cm^2, 19·6 cm   (d) 3 cm

BOOK 2   PART 6

Exercise 76 *page 67*   **1.** ab **2.** mn **3.** x^2 **4.** l^2 **5.** $6u$ **6.** $10v$
7. $2xy$ **8.** $3ab$ **9.** $2ab$ **10.** $3mn$ **11.** $5xy$ **12.** $6ab$
13. $10mn$ **14.** $12pq$ **15.** $9z^2$ **16.** $16t^2$

Exercise 77 *page 68*   **1.** (a) 24,   (b) 60,   (c) $12x$,   (d) $24x$
2. (a) 30,   (b) 60,   (c) $10x$,   (d) $30x$
3. (a) 100,   (b) 150,   (c) $50x$,   (d) $200x$
4. (a) 60,   (b) 100,   (c) $20y$,   (d) $200y$
5. (a) 80,   (b) 200,   (c) $40y$,   (d) $200y$
6. (a) 300,   (b) 600,   (c) $100x$,   (d) $400y$
7. (a) 50,   (b) 75,   (c) $25x$,   (d) $50y$
8. (a) 30,   (b) 60,   (c) $15p$,   (d) $60q$

Exercise 78 *page 69*   **1.** (a) $10x$ (b) $50x$ **2.** (a) $10y$ (b) $120y$
3. (a) $100z$ (b) $200z$
4. (a) 120   (b) 300   (c) $60m$ (d) $300m$
5. (a) 500   (b) 1000   (c) $100n$ (d) $1000n$
6. $20a + 20b$

Exercise 79   *page 69*

1. $x + 5$ 2. $y + 5$ 3. $a + 2$ 4. $4 + x$ 5. $3 + p$
6. $2 + t$ 7. $y + x$ 8. $x + y$ 9. $q + p$ 10. $6 + 2p$
11. $5 + 3q$ 12. $9 + 4x$ 13. $5a + 6$ 14. $3b + 8$ 15. $7c + 5$
16. $3a + 2b$ 17. $5x + 2y$ 18. $4p + 7q$ 19. $x - 5$ 20. $y - 5$
21. $a - 2$ 22. $4 - x$ 23. $3 - p$ 24. $2 - t$ 25. $y - x$
26. $x - y$ 27. $q - p$ 28. $p - q$ 29. $5a - 6$ 30. $2b - 7$
31. $9c - 4$ 32. $3 - 2m$ 33. $8 - 5n$ 34. $7 - 3p$ 35. $10 - 9q$
36. $3a - 2b$ 37. $5p - 8q$ 38. $7x - 4y$ 39. $4b - 3a$ 40. $9n - 2m$

Exercise 80   *page 70*

1. 7   2. 8   3. 11   4. 6   5. 6   6. 10   7. 5   8. 4
9. 8   10. 7   11. 12   12. 10   13. 5   14. 12   15. 10   16. 6
17. 6   18. 19   19. 1   20. 8   21. 1   22. 1   23. 20   24. 2
25. 2   26. 18   27. 2   28. 9   29. 16   30. 0   31. 11   32. 12
33. 23   34. 1   35. 15   36. 12   37. 7   38. 8   39. 14   40. 3
41. 18   42. 11   43. 13   44. 25   45. 27   46. 1   47. 10   48. 3
49. 3   50. 30   51. 16   52. 9   53. 20   54. 8   55. 9   56. 40
57. 3   58. 3   59. 500   60. 0

Exercise 81   *page 70*

1. 12   2. 14   3. 15   4. 8   5. 16   6. 24   7. 6   8. 18
9. 30   10. 12   11. 48   12. 24   13. 18   14. 6   15. 24   16. 120
17. 12   18. 24   19. 18   20. 90   21. 3   22. 9   23. 72   24. 12
25. 72   26. 24   27. 18   28. 12   29. 30   30. 0   31. 18   32. 36
33. 0   34. 0   35. 12   36. 6   37. 12   38. 48   39. 0   40. 36
41. 36   42. 0   43. 0   44. 0

Exercise 82   *page 71*

1. 4   2. 9   3. 8   4. 18   5. 16   6. 27   7. 8   8. 27
9. 18   10. 12   11. 16   12. 1   13. 48   14. 4   15. 80   16. 10
17. 64   18. 1   19. 4   20. 16

Exercise 83   *page 71*

1. 12   2. 30   3. 6   4. 10   5. 4   6. 2   7. 24   8. 36
9. 13   10. 5

Exercise 84   *page 72*

1. $2a$ 2. $3b$ 3. $4c$ 4. $6d$ 5. $3l$ 6. $4m$ 7. $6n$ 8. $4p$
9. $7q$ 10. $9r$ 11. $5t$ 12. $8u$ 13. $10v$ 14. $7x$ 15. $11y$ 16. $10a$
17. $15b$ 18. $12c$ 19. $12m$ 20. $10n$ 21. $12l$ 22. $15p$ 23. $20q$ 24. $2a$
25. $3b$ 26. $5c$ 27. $6l$ 28. $9m$ 29. $3n$ 30. $8p$ 31. $11q$ 32. r
33. t 34. u 35. v 36. $2a$ 37. $5b$ 38. $6c$ 39. $6l$ 40. m
41. 0   42. $3p$ 43. $2q$ 44. $4r$ 45. $4s$ 46. $3t$ 47. u 48. v
49. x 50. 0

Exercise 85   *page 72*

1. $6x + 5y$ 2. $8u + 7v$ 3. $9a + 2b$ 4. $7x + 4y$ 5. $7m^2 + 3m$
6. $9n^2 + 8n$ 7. $3u + 4v$ 8. $2x + 9y$ 9. $7p + 9q$ 10. $l + 7m$
11. $3z^2 + 4z$ 12. $5a^2 + 6a$ 13. $8b^2 + 5b$ 14. $7m + 9n$ 15. $5p + 12q$
16. $3u + 8v$ 17. $5x^2 + 9x$ 18. $7y^2 + 9y$ 19. $5l + 3m$ 20. $12b + 7c$
21. $7q + 8r$ 22. $12a + 11b$ 23. $10t^2 + 3t$ 24. $12u^2 + 5u$ 25. $3x + 7y$
26. $4a + 9b$ 27. $m + 8n$ 28. $5p + 4q$ 29. $6u + 5v$ 30. $3z^2 + 2z$
31. $9a + 7b$ 32. $9x + 6y$ 33. $9p + 4q$ 34. $4c + 3d$

Exercise 86   *page 73*

1. 4   2. 9   3. 16   4. 36   5. 100
6. 27   7. 216   8. 1000   9. 125   10. 1
11. 16   12. 32   13. 64   14. 16   15. 36
16. 100   17. 81   18. 81   19. 135   20. 225
21. 900   22. 1000   23. 125   24. 10 000   25. 2500

Exercise 87   *page 73*

1. 8^2
2. 7^2
3. 9^2
4. 6^3
5. 8^3
6. 10^3
7. 12^3
8. a^2
9. p^2
10. t^2
11. b^3
12. m^3
13. z^3
14. $2^2 \times 4^2$
15. $3^2 \times 5^2$
16. $6^2 \times 10^2$
17. $2^3 \times 7^2$
18. $4^3 \times 9^2$
19. $5^3 \times 6^2$
20. $2^2 \times 5^3$
21. $8^2 \times 9^3$
22. $x^2 \times y^2$
23. $m^2 \times n^2$
24. $u^2 \times v^2$
25. $a^3 \times b^2$
26. $y^3 \times z^2$
27. $u^3 \times v^2$
28. $m^2 \times n^3$
29. $p^2 \times q^3$
30. $c^2 \times d^3$

Exercise 88   *page 73*

1. x^3
2. y^3
3. a^3
4. b^3
5. $6p^2$
6. $20q^2$
7. $9r^2$
8. $6s^2$
9. $4x^3$
10. $7y^3$
11. $3a^3$
12. $9b^3$
13. $15m^3$
14. $12n^3$
15. $16t^3$
16. $6u^3$
17. $24v^3$
18. $20z^3$
19. $12a^3$
20. $14b^3$
21. $24c^3$
22. $9p^2$
23. $16q^2$
24. $4x^2$
25. $100y^2$

Exercise 89   *page 74*

1. 3
2. 2
3. 3
4. 4
5. 2
6. 2
7. 4
8. 3
9. 3
10. 7
11. 2
12. 4
13. 2
14. 3
15. 5
16. 3
17. 5
18. 8
19. 6
20. 9

Exercise 90   *page 74*

1. 2
2. 4
3. 6
4. 6
5. 4
6. 2
7. 8
8. 1
9. 3
10. 6
11. 5
12. 2
13. 5
14. 5
15. 7
16. 1
17. 8
18. 3
19. 2
20. 2
21. 3
22. 2
23. 5
24. 2
25. 6
26. 2
27. 5
28. 2
29. 3
30. 1
31. 4
32. 5
33. 8
34. 7
35. 5
36. 6
37. 7
38. 10
39. 12
40. 10

Exercise 91   *page 74*

1. 3
2. 5
3. 6
4. 7
5. 8
6. 9
7. 3
8. 20
9. 3
10. 2
11. 3
12. 4
13. 5
14. 4
15. 5
16. 6
17. 4
18. 5
19. 4
20. 9

Exercise 92   *page 75*

1. 3
2. 4
3. 6
4. 1
5. 2
6. 4
7. 5
8. 1
9. 3
10. 2
11. 4
12. 2
13. 1
14. 4
15. 3
16. 5
17. 6
18. 4
19. 4
20. 5
21. 2
22. 5
23. 3
24. 2
25. 3
26. 4
27. 5
28. 2
29. 3
30. 3

Revision exercise E
page 75

1. (b)
2. (a)
3. (a)
4. (c)
5. (b)
6. (a)
7. (c)
8. (b)
9. (c)
10. (a)
11. (a)
12. (b)
13. (c)
14. (b)
15. (c)
16. (a)
17. (b)
18. (a)
19. (c)
20. (b)
21. (a)

BOOK 2   PART 7

Exercise 93   *page 76*

1. (a) $A = \{1, 5, 10, 50\}$ (b) $B = \{10, 20, 30, 40, 50\}$
   (c) $A \cap B = \{10, 50\}$ (d) $A \cup B = \{1, 5, 10, 20, 30, 40, 50\}$

2. (a) $A = \{1, 5, 10, 50, 100\}$ (b) $B = \{20, 40, 60, 80, 100\}$
   (c) $A \cap B = \{100\}$ (d) $A \cup B = \{1, 5, 10, 20, 40, 50, 60, 80, 100\}$

3. (a) $A = \{15, 30, 40\}$ (b) $B = \{15, 30, 45, 60\}$
   (c) $A \cap B = \{15, 30\}$ (d) $A \cup B = \{15, 30, 40, 45, 60\}$

4. (a) $X = \{1, 2, 3, 4, 5, 6\}$ (b) $Y = \{2, 4, 6, 8, 10\}$
   (c) $X \cap Y = \{2, 4, 6\}$ (d) $X \cup Y = \{1, 2, 3, 4, 5, 6, 8, 10\}$

5. (a) $X = \{$India, Ireland, Italy$\}$
   (b) $Y = \{$England, Germany, Ireland$\}$ (c) $X \cap Y = \{$Ireland$\}$
   (d) $X \cup Y = \{$England, Germany, India, Ireland, Italy$\}$

6. (a) X = {Leeds, Leicester, Lincoln, Liverpool, London}
   (b) Y = {Edinburgh, Leicester, Liverpool, Newcastle, Sheffield}
   (c) X ∩ Y = {Leicester, Liverpool}

7. (a) P = {Bill, Fred, John}
   (b) Q = {Joe, John, Jim}   (c) P ∩ Q = {John}
   (d) P ∪ Q = {Bill, Fred, Joe, John, Jim}

8. (a) P = {Sally, Sandra, Sheila, Susan}
   (b) Q = {Diane, Karen, Sally, Susan}
   (c) P ∩ Q = {Sally, Susan}
   (d) P ∪ Q = {Diane, Karen, Sally, Sandra, Sheila, Susan}

9. (a) M = {Leeds United, Manchester United, West Ham United}
   (b) N = {Queen's Park Rangers, West Bromwich Albion, West Ham United}
   (c) M ∩ N = {West Ham United}

10. (a) M = {Birmingham City, Hull City, Manchester City, Norwich City, York City}
    (b) N = {Aston Villa, Hull City, Oxford United, Port Vale, York City}
    (c) M ∩ N = {Hull City, York City}

11. (a) A = {numbers up to 20 which divide by 3}
    (b) B = {numbers up to 20 which divide by 4}
    (c) A ∩ B = {numbers up to 20 which divide by 12}

12. (a) A = {numbers up to 30 which divide by 5}
    (b) B = {numbers up to 30 which divide by 6}
    (c) A ∩ B = {numbers up to 30 which divide by 30}

13. (a) A = {numbers up to 30 which divide by 4}
    (b) B = {numbers up to 30 which divide by 6}
    (c) A ∩ B = {numbers up to 30 which divide by 12}

14. (a) X = {square numbers up to 20}
    (b) Y = {triangular numbers up to 20}
    (c) X ∩ Y = {numbers up to 20 which are square and triangular}

15. (a) P = {animals of the cat family}
    (b) Q = {animals which are pets}
    (c) P ∩ Q = {animals of the cat family which are pets}

16. (a) X = {months with 30 days}
    (b) Y = {months whose names begin with A}
    (c) X ∩ Y = {months with 30 days whose names begin with A}

17. (a) A = {months with 31 days}
    (b) B = {months whose names begin with J}
    (c) A ∩ B = {months with 31 days whose names begin with J}

18. (a) X = {fried foods}   (b) Y = {foods made from potatoes}
    (c) X ∩ Y = {fried foods made from potatoes}

19. (a) M = {figures with 4 equal angles}
    (b) N = {figures with 4 equal sides}
    (c) M ∩ N = {figures with 4 equal angles and 4 equal sides}

20. (a) A = {items used in cricket}
    (b) B = {items used in tennis}
    (c) A ∩ B = {items used in both cricket and tennis}

Exercise 94   *page 79*

1.
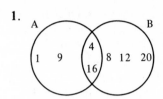

2.
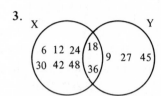

3.
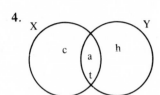

4.
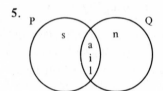

5.
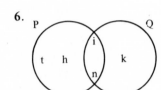

6.
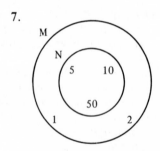

7.
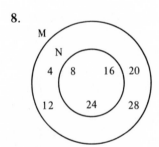

8.
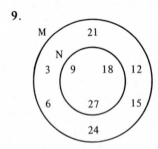

9.
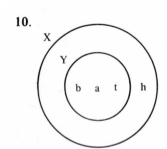

10.
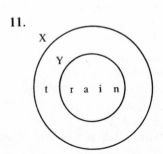

11.
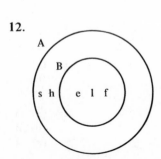

12.

13.

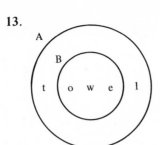

14.

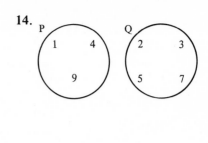

15.

P
$$\left(\begin{array}{ccc} f & l & y \end{array}\right)$$

Q
$$\left(\begin{array}{cccc} h & i & g & h \end{array}\right)$$

Exercise 95   *page 80*   **1.** 3 by 2   **2.** 3 by 3   **3.** 2 by 4   **4.** 2 by 1   **5.** 4 by 2
                                6. 4 by 4   **7.** 4 by 3   **8.** 4 by 1   **9.** 1 by 3   **10.** 1 by 5

Exercise 96   *page 81*

1. $\begin{pmatrix} 4 & 6 \\ 6 & 8 \end{pmatrix}$ **2.** $\begin{pmatrix} 7 & 8 \\ 5 & 10 \end{pmatrix}$ **3.** $\begin{pmatrix} 7 & 5 & 5 \\ 9 & 9 & 8 \end{pmatrix}$ **4.** $\begin{pmatrix} 9 & 11 & 6 \\ 12 & 5 & 9 \end{pmatrix}$

5. $\begin{pmatrix} 7 & 9 \\ 6 & 7 \\ 8 & 9 \end{pmatrix}$ **6.** $\begin{pmatrix} 12 & 10 \\ 10 & 5 \\ 6 & 11 \end{pmatrix}$ **7.** $\begin{pmatrix} 8 & 5 & 8 & 5 \\ 8 & 6 & 8 & 7 \end{pmatrix}$

8. $\begin{pmatrix} 10 & 9 & 10 & 4 \\ 12 & 9 & 9 & 11 \end{pmatrix}$ **9.** $\begin{pmatrix} 9 & 8 & 8 \\ 7 & 9 & 8 \\ 9 & 9 & 9 \end{pmatrix}$ **10.** not possible

11. $\begin{pmatrix} 3 & 2 \\ 2 & 1 \end{pmatrix}$ **12.** $\begin{pmatrix} 5 & 6 \\ 4 & 2 \end{pmatrix}$ **13.** $\begin{pmatrix} 3 & 3 & 3 \\ 2 & 3 & 4 \end{pmatrix}$ **14.** $\begin{pmatrix} 2 & 4 & 5 \\ 7 & 4 & 2 \end{pmatrix}$

15. $\begin{pmatrix} 6 & 5 \\ 2 & 1 \\ 2 & 2 \end{pmatrix}$ **16.** $\begin{pmatrix} 2 & 6 \\ 3 & 7 \\ 5 & 2 \end{pmatrix}$ **17.** $\begin{pmatrix} 3 & 2 & 2 & 2 \\ 6 & 2 & 1 & 0 \end{pmatrix}$

18. not possible   **19.** $\begin{pmatrix} 4 & 3 & 3 \\ 3 & 2 & 2 \\ 3 & 2 & 8 \end{pmatrix}$ **20.** $\begin{pmatrix} 1 & 1 & 5 \\ 4 & 3 & 1 \\ 4 & 0 & 1 \end{pmatrix}$

Exercise 97   *page 82*

1. $\begin{pmatrix} 10 & 7 \\ 10 & 5 \end{pmatrix}$ **2.** $\begin{pmatrix} 8 & 5 \\ 6 & 3 \end{pmatrix}$ **3.** $\begin{pmatrix} 18 & 12 \\ 15 & 9 \end{pmatrix}$ **4.** $\begin{pmatrix} 12 & 8 \\ 11 & 5 \end{pmatrix}$

5. $\begin{pmatrix} 16 & 11 \\ 15 & 8 \end{pmatrix}$ **6.** $\begin{pmatrix} 10 & 6 \\ 7 & 3 \end{pmatrix}$ **7.** $\begin{pmatrix} 8 & 6 \\ 10 & 4 \end{pmatrix}$ **8.** $\begin{pmatrix} 16 & 11 \\ 16 & 7 \end{pmatrix}$

9. $\begin{pmatrix} 2 & 1 \\ 0 & 1 \end{pmatrix}$ **10.** $\begin{pmatrix} 4 & 3 \\ 4 & 3 \end{pmatrix}$ **11.** $\begin{pmatrix} 6 & 3 \\ 3 & 0 \end{pmatrix}$ **12.** $\begin{pmatrix} 8 & 6 \\ 9 & 5 \end{pmatrix}$

13. $\begin{pmatrix} 14 & 9 \\ 10 & 7 \end{pmatrix}$ **14.** $\begin{pmatrix} 0 & 1 \\ 2 & 3 \end{pmatrix}$ **15.** $\begin{pmatrix} 24 & 16 \\ 20 & 12 \end{pmatrix}$ **16.** $\begin{pmatrix} 6 & 5 \\ 8 & 5 \end{pmatrix}$

17. $\begin{pmatrix} 8 & 6 \\ 5 & 3 \end{pmatrix}$ **18.** $\begin{pmatrix} 7 & 5 \\ 4 & 3 \end{pmatrix}$ **19.** $\begin{pmatrix} 20 & 16 \\ 16 & 8 \end{pmatrix}$ **20.** $\begin{pmatrix} 10 & 7 \\ 5 & 4 \end{pmatrix}$

21. $\begin{pmatrix} 19 & 14 \\ 11 & 7 \end{pmatrix}$ **22.** $\begin{pmatrix} 18 & 12 \\ 8 & 8 \end{pmatrix}$ **23.** $\begin{pmatrix} 18 & 12 \\ 6 & 6 \end{pmatrix}$ **24.** $\begin{pmatrix} 6 & 5 \\ 5 & 2 \end{pmatrix}$

25. $\begin{pmatrix} 2 & 2 \\ 3 & 1 \end{pmatrix}$ **26.** $\begin{pmatrix} 3 & 3 \\ 4 & 1 \end{pmatrix}$ **27.** $\begin{pmatrix} 14 & 7 \\ 0 & 7 \end{pmatrix}$ **28.** $\begin{pmatrix} 9 & 7 \\ 6 & 3 \end{pmatrix}$

29. $\begin{pmatrix} 3 & 4 \\ 8 & 2 \end{pmatrix}$ **30.** $\begin{pmatrix} 11 & 10 \\ 12 & 4 \end{pmatrix}$ **31.** $\begin{pmatrix} 25 & 20 \\ 20 & 10 \end{pmatrix}$ **32.** $\begin{pmatrix} 2 & 3 \\ 5 & 0 \end{pmatrix}$

33. $\begin{pmatrix} 7 & 5 & 9 \\ 5 & 3 & 7 \end{pmatrix}$ **34.** not possible   **35.** $\begin{pmatrix} 20 & 14 \\ 15 & 10 \end{pmatrix}$ **36.** not possible

37. $\begin{pmatrix} 1 & 2 & 0 \\ 2 & 3 & 1 \end{pmatrix}$ **38.** not possible   **39.** $\begin{pmatrix} 10 & 8 \\ 5 & 5 \end{pmatrix}$ **40.** not possible

41. $\begin{pmatrix} 4 & 2 \\ 5 & 2 \end{pmatrix}$ **42.** $\begin{pmatrix} 22 & 16 \\ 15 & 11 \end{pmatrix}$ **43.** not possible

44. $\begin{pmatrix} 16 & 11 & 21 \\ 11 & 6 & 16 \end{pmatrix}$ **45.** $\begin{pmatrix} 24 & 18 & 30 \\ 18 & 12 & 24 \end{pmatrix}$ **46.** $\begin{pmatrix} 48 & 34 \\ 35 & 24 \end{pmatrix}$

47. not possible   **48.** $\begin{pmatrix} 2 & 4 & 0 \\ 4 & 6 & 2 \end{pmatrix}$ **49.** $\begin{pmatrix} 12 & 10 \\ 5 & 6 \end{pmatrix}$

50. not possible

answers

BOOK 3   PART 1

Exercise 1   *page 1*

1. 879   2. 726   3. 984   4. 865   5. 926   6. 751
7. (a)   8. (d)   9. (c)   10. (a)   11. (b)   12. (c)
13. (c)   14. (d)   15. (a)   16. (b)   17. (d)   18. (c)
19. 423   20. 245   21. 154   22. 51   23. 324   24. 276
25. (b)   26. (c)   27. (d)   28. (b)   29. (a)   30. (a)
31. (c)   32. (b)   33. 312 + 452 + 323   34. 534 + 313 + 232
35. 331 + 243 + 612   36. 835 + 320 + 143   37. 513 + 342 + 402
38. 8985 − 6362   39. 8878 − 3632   40. 9565 − 2402
41. 8928 − 5520   42. 3969 − 1259   43. 9967 − 3125
44. 4897 − 4520

Exercise 2   *page 2*

1. 1424   2. 1265   3. 1206   4. 1920   5. 1215   6. 1421
7. 2580   8. 3150   9. (c)   10. (a)   11. (b)   12. (d)
13. (c)   14. (b)   15. 231   16. 216   17. 131   18. 247
19. 206   20. 130   21. 31   22. 22   23. (a)   24. (b)
25. (d)   26. (c)   27. (a)   28. (c)   29. 48 × 4   30. 32 × 8
31. 132 × 3   32. 218 × 4   33. 134 × 5   34. 375 ÷ 5   35. 612 ÷ 9
36. 625 ÷ 5   37. 726 ÷ 3   38. 832 ÷ 4   39. 720 ÷ 6   40. 810 ÷ 9

Exercise 3   *page 2*

1. (a) 108 cm,   (b) 12 cm,   (c) 84 cm
2. (a) 982 m,   (b) 8838 m   3. 65 g   4. 300 g
5. (a) 625 km,   (b) 434 km,   (c) 217 km,   (d) 842 km
6. 448 m, 319 m   7. 9570, 3190, 290   8. 470 m, 94 m   9. 8 g

Exercise 4   *page 4*

1. 6   2. 14   3. 30   4. 12   5. 140   6. 24
7. 40   8. 36   9. 15   10. 105   11. 45   12. 75
13. 2 × 3 × 7   14. 2 × 2 × 3 × 5   15. 2 × 2 × 5 × 11
16. 2 × 2 × 5 × 5   17. 2 × 2 × 2 × 3 × 11   18. 2 × 2 × 2 × 5 × 7
19. 2 × 2 × 2 × 2 × 5 × 5   20. 3 × 5 × 11   21. 3 × 7 × 11
22. 3 × 3 × 7   23. 3 × 3 × 5 × 7   24. 5 × 5 × 11

Exercise 5   *page 4*

1. 6   2. 4   3. 9   4. 6   5. 9   6. 8
7. 8   8. 4   9. 6   10. 8   11. 12   12. 20
13. 4   14. 6   15. 8   16. 9   17. 8   18. 6

Exercise 6   *page 4*

1. 2 × 7 = 14   2. 2 × 5 × 7 = 70   3. 2 × 2 × 3 = 12
4. 2 × 2 × 2 × 5 = 40   5. 2 × 2 × 2 × 7 = 56   6. 2 × 2 × 2 × 2 = 16
7. 3 × 3 = 9   8. 3 × 7 = 21   9. 2 × 2 × 5 × 5 = 100
10. 2 × 3 × 5 × 5 = 150

Exercise 7 *page 5*

1. 22 2. 42 3. 44 4. 24 5. 24 6. 16 7. 36 8. 12
9. 33 10. 63 11. 14 12. 22 13. 12 14. 56 15. 21 16. 30

Exercise 8 *page 5*

1. 6 2. 10 3. 24 4. 4 5. 8 6. 6 7. 9 8. 12
9. 30 10. 20 11. 40 12. 36 13. 12 14. 20 15. 12 16. 6
17. 12 18. 12 19. 30 20. 24

Exercise 9 *page 5*

1. $2 \times 5 \times 5 = 50$ 2. $2 \times 2 \times 3 \times 5 = 60$ 3. $2 \times 2 \times 3 \times 7 = 84$
4. $2 \times 2 \times 2 \times 7 = 56$ 5. $2 \times 2 \times 5 \times 5 = 100$ 6. $2 \times 3 \times 3 \times 5 = 90$
7. $2 \times 2 \times 2 \times 3 \times 5 = 120$ 8. $2 \times 2 \times 2 \times 2 \times 5 = 80$
9. $2 \times 2 \times 2 \times 2 \times 5 = 80$ 10. $2 \times 2 \times 2 \times 3 \times 3 = 72$

Exercise 10 *page 6*

1. 70 2. 75 3. 60 4. 90 5. 60 6. 54
7. 72 8. 48 9. 80 10. 108 11. 90 12. 60
13. 120 14. 60 15. 90 16. 180 17. 90 18. 120

Exercise 11 *page 6*

1. $\frac{3}{4}$ 2. $\frac{3}{4}$ 3. $\frac{2}{3}$ 4. $\frac{5}{6}$ 5. $\frac{11}{15}$ 6. $1\frac{1}{6}$ 7. $1\frac{3}{4}$ 8. $\frac{1}{4}$
9. $\frac{3}{4}$ 10. $\frac{1}{3}$ 11. $\frac{4}{15}$ 12. $\frac{1}{6}$ 13. $\frac{1}{6}$ 14. $\frac{1}{10}$ 15. $\frac{2}{3}$ 16. $\frac{2}{9}$
17. $\frac{3}{4}$ 18. $\frac{6}{25}$ 19. $\frac{4}{5}$ 20. $\frac{5}{12}$ 21. $\frac{5}{12}$ 22. $1\frac{1}{3}$ 23. $1\frac{1}{2}$ 24. $1\frac{1}{5}$

Exercise 12 *page 6*

1. $\frac{4}{3}$ 2. $\frac{7}{6}$ 3. $\frac{5}{3}$ 4. $\frac{9}{5}$ 5. $\frac{9}{4}$ 6. $\frac{8}{3}$ 7. $\frac{19}{6}$ 8. $\frac{15}{4}$
9. $\frac{14}{3}$ 10. $\frac{21}{4}$ 11. $1\frac{1}{4}$ 12. $1\frac{1}{5}$ 13. $1\frac{3}{5}$ 14. $1\frac{3}{4}$ 15. $2\frac{1}{3}$ 16. $2\frac{3}{4}$
17. $3\frac{1}{2}$ 18. $3\frac{2}{3}$ 19. $4\frac{1}{3}$ 20. $5\frac{3}{4}$

Exercise 13 *page 7*

1. $1\frac{1}{2}$ 2. $1\frac{2}{3}$ 3. $1\frac{3}{4}$ 4. $1\frac{5}{6}$ 5. $2\frac{3}{4}$ 6. $2\frac{1}{6}$ 7. $3\frac{1}{2}$ 8. $2\frac{3}{4}$
9. $4\frac{1}{3}$ 10. $3\frac{2}{3}$ 11. $\frac{3}{4}$ 12. $\frac{1}{3}$ 13. $\frac{1}{3}$ 14. $\frac{2}{3}$ 15. $\frac{5}{6}$ 16. $1\frac{1}{4}$
17. $2\frac{1}{5}$ 18. $\frac{3}{4}$ 19. $1\frac{1}{10}$ 20. $1\frac{1}{6}$ 21. (c) 22. (b) 23. (a) 24. (b)
25. (c) 26. (b) 27. (b) 28. (a) 29. (b) 30. (a)

Exercise 14 *page 7*

1. $\frac{2}{3}$ 2. $\frac{3}{4}$ 3. $\frac{2}{3}$ 4. $1\frac{2}{3}$ 5. $1\frac{1}{2}$ 6. $3\frac{1}{2}$ 7. $2\frac{2}{3}$ 8. $2\frac{1}{4}$
9. 6 10. $\frac{8}{15}$ 11. $\frac{2}{3}$ 12. $\frac{3}{4}$ 13. $1\frac{1}{2}$ 14. $1\frac{3}{4}$ 15. 4 16. $\frac{1}{6}$
17. $\frac{3}{4}$ 18. $4\frac{1}{2}$ 19. $7\frac{1}{2}$ 20. $\frac{9}{20}$ 21. (c) 22. (b) 23. (a) 24. (c)
25. (c) 26. (b) 27. (b) 28. (a) 29. (b) 30. (a)

Exercise 15 *page 8*

1. 5 km 2. 7 cm, $1\frac{3}{4}$ cm 3. $1\frac{4}{5}$ m 4. 20 g 5. $2\frac{1}{4}$ g

Exercise 16 *page 8*

1. (a) 2. (b) 3. (b) 4. (c) 5. (a) 6. (a) 7. (c) 8. (b)
9. (a) 10. (b) 11. (a) 12. (b) 13. (b) 14. (c) 15. (b) 16. (a)
17. (b) 18. (a) 19. (b) 20. (c) 21. $\frac{9}{10}$ 22. $\frac{3}{5}$ 23. $\frac{1}{5}$ 24. $\frac{3}{20}$
25. $\frac{13}{20}$ 26. $\frac{7}{25}$ 27. $\frac{16}{25}$ 28. $\frac{1}{25}$ 29. $\frac{3}{50}$ 30. $\frac{13}{40}$ 31. 0·14 32. 0·58
33. 0·32 34. 0·84 35. 0·68 36. 0·102 37. 0·126 38. 0·155
39. 0·265 40. 0·168

Exercise 17 *page 9*

1. (b) 2. (c) 3. (b) 4. (a) 5. (a) 6. (c) 7. (a) 8. (c)
9. (b) 10. (b) 11. (a) 12. (b) 13. (c) 14. (b) 15. (a) 16. (c)

Exercise 18 *page 9*

1. (a) 172·8, (b) 172·8, (c) 1728
2. (a) 43·2, (b) 43·2, (c) 432
3. (a) 49, (b) 49, (c) 490
4. (a) 90, (b) 90, (c) 900
5. (a) 19·38, (b) 19·38, (c) 1938
6. (a) 3·36, (b) 3·36, (c) 336
7. (a) 18, (b) 18, (c) 1800
8. (a) 1·296, (b) 1·296, (c) 12·96
9. (a) 0·276, (b) 0·276, (c) 2·76, (d) 2·76, (e) 2·76 (f) 276
10. (a) 0·54 (b) 0·54, (c) 5·4, (d) 5·4, (e) 5·4, (f) 540
11. (a) 57·6, (b) 57·6, (c) 5·76
12. (a) 248·5, (b) 248·5, (c) 24·85
13. (a) 162, (b) 162 (c) 16·2
14. (a) 130, (b) 130, (c) 13
15. (a) 1·512, (b) 1·512, (c) 0·1512
16. (a) 0·435, (b) 0·435, (c) 0·0435
17. (a) 13·68, (b) 13·68, (c) 0·1368
18. (a) 27, (b) 27, (c) 0·27
19. (a) 6, (b) 6, (c) 0·06
20. (a) 260, (b) 260, (c) 26, (d) 26, (e) 26, (f) 0·26

Exercise 19 *page 10*

1. $\frac{3}{100}$ 2. $\frac{11}{100}$ 3. $\frac{39}{100}$ 4. $\frac{53}{100}$ 5. $\frac{81}{100}$ 6. $\frac{21}{50}$

7. $\frac{19}{50}$ 8. $\frac{43}{50}$ 9. $\frac{9}{20}$ 10. $\frac{13}{20}$ 11. $\frac{8}{25}$ 12. $\frac{14}{25}$

13. $\frac{1}{25}$ 14. $\frac{9}{10}$ 15. $\frac{1}{5}$ 16. $\frac{17}{40}$ 17. $\frac{29}{40}$ 18. $\frac{5}{8}$

19. $\frac{2}{15}$ 20. $\frac{1}{15}$ 21. $\frac{8}{15}$ 22. $\frac{2}{3}$ 23. $\frac{7}{12}$ 24. $\frac{13}{80}$

25. $\frac{13}{16}$ 26. $1\frac{11}{50}$ 27. $1\frac{9}{25}$ 28. $1\frac{7}{20}$ 29. $1\frac{1}{4}$ 30. $1\frac{3}{5}$

Exercise 20 *page 11*

1. 0·18 2. 0·26 3. 0·37 4. 0·41 5. 0·67 6. 0·84
7. 0·8 8. 0·6 9. 0·3 10. 0·1 11. 0·08 12. 0·05
13. 0·02 14. 0·01 15. 0·325 16. 0·125 17. 0·875 18. 0·045
19. 0·3125 20. 0·5625 21. 0·1875 22. 0·7375 23. 1·25 24. 1·82
25. 1·55 26. 1·4 27. 1·1 28. 1·05 29. 1·225 30. 1·575

Exercise 21 *page 11*

1. 30% 2. 90% 3. 10% 4. 60% 5. 20% 6. 14%
7. 22% 8. 34% 9. 58% 10. 15% 11. 35% 12. 5%

13. 55% 14. 36% 15. 48% 16. $12\frac{1}{2}$% 17. $11\frac{1}{9}$% 18. $16\frac{2}{3}$%

19. $46\frac{2}{3}$% 20. $73\frac{1}{3}$% 21. $93\frac{1}{3}$% 22. $86\frac{2}{3}$% 23. $41\frac{2}{3}$% 24. $77\frac{1}{2}$%

25. $57\frac{1}{2}$% 26. 140% 27. 175% 28. 120% 29. $112\frac{1}{2}$% 30. $133\frac{1}{3}$%

Exercise 22 *page 11*

1. 15% 2. 29% 3. 48% 4. 53% 5. 76% 6. 93%
7. 90% 8. 70% 9. 40% 10. 20% 11. 9% 12. 6%

13. 4% 14. $62\frac{1}{2}$% 15. $57\frac{1}{2}$% 16. $22\frac{1}{2}$% 17. $7\frac{1}{2}$% 18. $1\frac{1}{2}$%

19. $26\frac{1}{4}$% 20. $81\frac{1}{4}$% 21. $43\frac{3}{4}$% 22. $6\frac{1}{4}$% 23. 175% 24. 164%

25. 111% 26. 120% 27. 150% 28. 108% 29. $162\frac{1}{2}$% 30. $117\frac{1}{2}$%

Exercise 23 *page 12*

1. 11 2. 9 3. 25 4. 95 5. 53 cm 6. 75 kg
7. 59 g 8. 48 p 9. £33 10. £2 11. £75 12. £4
13. £1 14. £33 15. 2 m 16. 1 m 17. £72 18. 13 years

19. 11 years **20.** 15   **21.** 44   **22.** 9 kg   **23.** 12 cm   **24.** 10 cm
25. (a) 13,   (b) 14,   (c) 135,   (d) 27

Exercise 24   *page 14*

1. 18·4   **2.** 29·2   **3.** 13·5 g   **4.** £7·50
5. 14·5 kg   **6.** £13·60   **7.** 3·5   **8.** 6·5 m
9. £2·16   **10.** 99 p   **11.** 30·5   **12.** 1 m 78 cm
13. £75·20   **14.** £27·60   **15.** 17 cm 4 mm   **16.** 11 cm 7 mm
17. 21 kg 600 g   **18.** 9 l 950 ml

Revision exercise A
page 14

1. 200 g   **2.** 300 g   **3.** (a) 48 km,   (b) 10 km
4. (a) 565 mm,   (b) 180 g   **5.** (a) 15 cm,   (b) 3 cm
6. (a) $1\frac{1}{5}$ m, 120 cm,   (b) $7\frac{1}{2}$ cm
7. (a) $\frac{1}{4}$, 25%,   (b) $\frac{2}{5}$, 40%   (c) $\frac{7}{20}$, 35%
8. (a) $\frac{1}{4}$, 25%   (b) $\frac{1}{10}$, 10%,   (c) $\frac{1}{5}$, 20%   (d) $\frac{9}{20}$, 45%
9. Julie, by 1 mark
10. (a) 4,   (b) 3,   (c) 1,   (d) 43, 21, 24, 12,   (e) 25

BOOK 3   PART 2

Exercise 25   *page 16*

1. $\hat{b}, \hat{c}, \hat{y}, \hat{z}$ **2.** $\hat{m}, \hat{n}, \hat{q}, \hat{r}$ **3.** $\hat{c}, \hat{d}, \hat{u}, \hat{v}$ **4.** $\hat{r}, \hat{q}, \hat{z}, \hat{y}$
5. $\hat{c}, \hat{b}, \hat{y}, \hat{z}$ **6.** $\hat{m}, \hat{n}, \hat{r}, \hat{q}$

Exercise 26   *page 17*

1. $\hat{c}, \hat{d}$ **2.** $\hat{r}, \hat{s}$ **3.** $\hat{m}, \hat{n}$ **4.** $\hat{x}, \hat{y}$ **5.** $\hat{p}, \hat{q}$ **6.** $\hat{s}, \hat{r}$

Exercise 27   *page 17*

1. 130°   **2.** 120°   **3.** 110°, 70°   **4.** 140°, 140°
5. 80°, 80°   **6.** 60°   **7.** 110°   **8.** 80°
9. 70°   **10.** 50°   **11.** 60°, 120°   **12.** 110°, 70°, 110°
13. 150°, 30°, 30°   **14.** 40°, 140°, 140°   **15.** 50°, 50°, 130°   **16.** 120°, 120°, 60°

Exercise 28   *page 18*

1. $\hat{p}, \hat{q}$ **2.** $\hat{x}, \hat{y}$ **3.** $\hat{v}, \hat{u}$ **4.** $\hat{s}, \hat{r}$ **5.** $\hat{x}, \hat{y}$ **6.** $\hat{u}, \hat{y}$

Exercise 29   *page 19*

1. 60°   **2.** 130°   **3.** 40°   **4.** 110°
5. 80°   **6.** 60°, 60°   **7.** 140°, 140°   **8.** 50°, 130°
9. 70°, 110°   **10.** 120°, 60°   **11.** 50°, 50°   **12.** 140°, 140°, 40°
13. 110°, 110°, 70°   **14.** 120°, 120°   **15.** 120°, 120°, 120°
16. 130°, 50°

Exercise 30   *page 20*

1. $\hat{x}, \hat{y}$ **2.** $\hat{r}, \hat{s}$ **3.** $\hat{z}, \hat{y}$ **4.** $\hat{y}, \hat{x}$ **5.** $\hat{u}, \hat{v}$ **6.** $\hat{p}, \hat{q}$

Exercise 31   *page 20*

1. 120°   **2.** 50°   **3.** 110°   **4.** 40°
5. 100°, 80°   **6.** 60°, 120°   **7.** 130°, 130°   **8.** 70°, 70°
9. 140°, 40°   **10.** 80°, 100°   **11.** 50°, 130°   **12.** 110°, 70°
13. 60°, 120°, 60°   **14.** 130°, 50°, 130°   **15.** 70°, 110°, 110°
16. 140°, 40°, 40°   **17.** 60°, 120°, 120°   **18.** 100°, 80°, 80°

Exercise 32   *page 22*

1. B   **2.** C   **3.** E   **4.** F   **5.** G   **6.** D   **7.** A   **8.** C
9. B   **10.** E   **11.** G   **12.** F   **13.** B   **14.** C   **15.** G

Exercise 33 *page 23*
1. 50°, 80°   2. 65°, 50°   3. 35°, 110°   4. 32°, 116°
5. 55°, 55°   6. 72°, 72°   7. 25°, 25°   8. 36°, 36°
9. 150°, 75°, 75°   10. 124°, 62°, 62°   11. 40°, 70°, 70°
12. 76°, 52°, 52°   13. 66°, 48°, 132°   14. 48°, 84°, 96°
15. 75°, 30°, 150°   16. 54°, 72°, 108°

Exercise 34 *page 24*
1. 50°   2. 110°   3. 60°   4. 125°
5. 40°, 80°, 60°   6. 30°, 80°, 80°   7. 50°, 60°, 70°
8. 55°, 55°, 45°   9. 45°, 65°, 65°   10. 45°, 60°, 75°
11. 35°, 35°, 95°   12. 70°, 55°, 55°   13. 70°, 70°, 70°, 70°
14. 40°, 40°, 40°, 40°   15. 45°, 90°, 45°, 90°   16. 45°, 45°, 90°, 90°

Revision exercise B
page 25
1. 55°, 95°, 30°, 150°   2. 65°, 25°, 90°   3. 75°, 75°, 75°, 75°, 30°
4. 45°, 135°, 45°, 45°   5. 90°, 90°, 60°, 30°   6. 105°, 75°, 120°, 60°, 45°
7. 95°, 85°, 85°, 140°, 40°, 55°   8. 65°, 65°, 115°, 65°, 65°, 50°
9. 30°, 30°, 90°, 90°, 90°   10. 30°, 60°, 60°
11. 80°, 60°, 60°, 40°   12. 25°, 130°, 130°, 25°, 155°

BOOK 3   PART 3

Exercise 35 *page 27*
1. (a) 4, 8, 5, 7, 3, 1   (b) 15   (c) 27   (d) 50
2. (a) 6, 11, 15, 4, 3   (b) 25   (c) 10   (d) 50
3. (a) 21   (b) 30   4. (a) 38   (b) 50

Exercise 36 *page 30*
1. 330   2. (a) 120   (b) £300   3. (a) 200   (b) £250

Exercise 37 *page 33*
1. 80, 60, 50, 30, 20   2. 60, 50, 40, 30

Exercise 38 *page 35*
1. 15   2. 1   3. 4   4. 2   5. 4   6. 5   7. 1   8. 25
9. 17   10. 2

Exercise 39 *page 36*
1. 5   2. 16 litres   3. 33   4. 58 p   5. 19, 10
6. 22°C   7. 53 km   8. 200   9. 40 days   10. 17

Exercise 40 *page 37*
1. 21   2. 110   3. 4, 2   4. 3   5. 18
6. 4   7. 61   8. 13, 11   9. 10   10. 105
11. 3   12. 2   13. 1 h   14. 2 h   15. 45 857

Exercise 41 *page 39*

1. 3←5   11   2. 2——←6←10   3. 16   13←9
   ↑   ↓   ↑   ↑   ↑
   4   7←9   12   18→14   12   0   5
   ↑   ↑   ↑   ↓   ↑
   6←8←10   16←20←24   8←4   1

4. 24   6←0   5. 3   7←14   6. 9→3→1
   ↑   ↓   ↑   ↑   ↑
   18←12   10   6   48   28   27   54   2
            ↓   ↑   ↑   ↑   ↑   ↓   ↑
   28←22←16   12←24   56   81   18→6

7.
$$64 \leftarrow 32 \quad 48$$
$$8 \rightarrow 16 \quad 24$$
$$4 \qquad 6 \rightarrow 12$$

8.
$$64 \leftarrow 16 \leftarrow 4$$
$$32 \qquad \tfrac{1}{4} \rightarrow 1$$
$$8 \leftarrow 2 \leftarrow \tfrac{1}{2}$$

Exercise 42 *page 40*

1. 'is a factor of'	**2.** 'is a factor of'
3. 'is a multiple of'	**4.** 'is the square of'
5. 'is a multiple of'	**6.** 'is a prime factor of'
7. 'is a multiple of'	**8.** 'is the square of'
9. 'is a multiple of'	**10.** 'is a prime factor of'

Exercise 45 *page 41*

1. $x > 7$ **2.** $x > 5$ **3.** $y > 9$ **4.** $x \geqslant 4$ **5.** $x \geqslant 9$
6. $a \geqslant 1$ **7.** $b \geqslant 8$ **8.** $x < 4$ **9.** $p < 6$ **10.** $q < 2$
11. $r < 10$ **12.** $x \leqslant 4$ **13.** $a \leqslant 9$ **14.** $b \leqslant 3$ **15.** $c \leqslant 12$

Revision exercise C
page 42

1. mean   **2.** mode   **3.** mode   **4.** median   **5.** mean
6. median   **7.** median   **8.** mode   **9.** mean   **10.** mode
11. 8, 5, 3, 6, 4, 4

13.
$$1 \leftarrow 6 \leftarrow 11$$
$$3 \leftarrow 8 \quad 16$$
$$18 \rightarrow 13 \quad 21$$

14.
$$15 \leftarrow 12 \quad 16$$
$$6 \rightarrow 9 \quad 13$$
$$3 \qquad 7 \rightarrow 10$$

15. 'is a factor of'   **16.** 'is a multiple of'
17. 'is the square of'   **18.** 'is the square root of'
19. 'is the L.C.M. of'   **20.** 'is the H.C.F. of'

BOOK 3   PART 4

Exercise 46 *page 44*

1. 300 cm², 74 cm   **2.** 900 mm², 150 mm   **3.** 9 m², 12·5 m
4. 6000 cm², 340 cm   **5.** 625 mm², 100 mm   **6.** 45 cm²
7. 2800 mm²   **8.** 700 cm²   **9.** 1·2 m²
10. 3150 mm²   **11.** 900 mm², 200 mm   **12.** 1000 mm²
13. 225 mm², 100 mm   **14.** 10 m², £57   **15.** 45 m², 4·5 litres
16. 3200 cm²

Exercise 47 *page 45*

1. 55 cm²   **2.** 21 cm²   **3.** 25 cm²   **4.** 780 mm²
5. 425 mm²   **6.** 1300 mm²   **7.** 4·8 m²   **8.** 0·6 m²
9. 28 cm²   **10.** 57 cm²   **11.** 100 cm²   **12.** 250 mm²
13. 650 mm²   **14.** 1·8 m²   **15.** 0·6 m²   **16.** 6000 cm²
17. 140 cm²   **18.** 800 mm²   **19.** 225 mm²   **20.** 0·6 m²
21. 84 cm²   **22.** 300 cm²   **23.** 350 mm²   **24.** 0·2 m²
25. 120 cm²

Exercise 48 *page 47*

1. 15 cm²   **2.** 28 cm²   **3.** 54 cm²   **4.** 160 mm²
5. 3 m²   **6.** 48 cm²   **7.** 120 cm²   **8.** 300 cm²

9. 600 mm^2 10. 2000 mm^2 11. 1000 mm^2 12. 9·6 m^2
13. 7·5 m^2 14. 5·4 cm^2 15. 27 cm^2 16. 30 m^2
17. 14 m^2 18. 6 m^2 19. 8 m^2 20. 1·8 cm^2

Exercise 49 *page 49*
1. 6 cm   2. 8 cm   3. 7 cm   4. 3 cm   5. 9 cm
6. 6 cm   7. 40 mm   8. 60 mm   9. 25 mm   10. 45 mm
11. 35 mm   12. 4 cm   13. 3 cm   14. 4 cm   15. 6 cm
16. 3 m   17. 5 m   18. 8 m   19. 2·5 m   20. 1·5 m

Exercise 50 *page 50*
1. 12 cm^2 2. 32 cm^2 3. 50 cm^2 4. 60 cm^2
5. 200 mm^2 6. 2 m^2 7. 26 m^2 8. 8 cm^2
9. 20 cm^2 10. 84 cm^2 11. 5 m^2 12. 550 mm^2

Exercise 51 *page 51*
1. 40 cm^2 2. 60 cm^2 3. 72 cm^2 4. 60 cm^2
5. 30 cm^2 6. 300 mm^2 7. 50 mm^2 8. 14 m^2
9. 56 mm^2 10. 72 cm^2 11. 84 cm^2 12. 840 mm^2
13. 1200 mm^2 14. 30 cm^2 15. 24 cm^2 16. 72 cm^2

Exercise 52 *page 53*
1. 7 m^2 2. 46 m^2 3. 52 m^2, 130   4. 15 m^2, 12
5. 2100 cm^2 6. 160 cm^2 7. 900 cm^2 8. 68 m^2
9. 168 mm^2 10. 46 cm^2 11. 100 cm^2, 90 cm^2, 900 mm^2, 9 cm^2

BOOK 3   PART 5

Exercise 53 *page 56*
1. 15°C   2. 19°C   3. 15°C   4. 12°C   5. 13°C
6. 11°C   7. +2°   8. −4°   9. −7°   10. 8°C
11. 11°C   12. −6°C   13. −2°C   14. −1°C   15. −6°
16. −5°   17. 2°C   18. 5°C   19. 4°C   20. 3°C
21. +9°   22. +6°   23. −2°C   24. −1°C   25. −7°C
26. −9°C   27. −2°   28. −6°   29. −3°C   30. −4°C

Exercise 54 *page 57*

1.
add	6	4	2	0	−2	−4	−6
4	10	8	6	4	2	0	−2
2	8	6	4	2	0	−2	−4
0	6	4	2	0	−2	−4	−6
−2	4	2	0	−2	−4	−6	−8
−4	2	0	−2	−4	−6	−8	−10
−6	0	−2	−4	−6	−8	−10	−12

2.
add	9	6	3	0	−3	−6	−9
6	15	12	9	6	3	0	−3
3	12	9	6	3	0	−3	−6
0	9	6	3	0	−3	−6	−9
−3	6	3	0	−3	−6	−9	−12
−6	3	0	−3	−6	−9	−12	−15
−9	0	−3	−6	−9	−12	−15	−18

3.

add	5	3	2	0	−2	−3	−5
2	7	5	4	2	0	−1	−3
0	5	3	2	0	−2	−3	−5
−2	3	1	0	−2	−4	−5	−7
−3	2	0	−1	−3	−5	−6	−8
−5	0	−2	−3	−5	−7	−8	−10
−7	−2	−4	−5	−7	−9	−10	−12

4.

add	9	4	1	0	−1	−4	−9
4	13	8	5	4	3	0	−5
1	10	5	2	1	0	−3	−8
0	9	4	1	0	−1	−4	−9
−1	8	3	0	−1	−2	−5	−10
−4	5	0	−3	−4	−5	−8	−13
−9	0	−5	−8	−9	−10	−13	−18

5.

add	6	3	1	0	−1	−3	−6
3	9	6	4	3	2	0	−3
1	7	4	2	1	0	−2	−5
0	6	3	1	0	−1	−3	−6
−1	5	2	0	−1	−2	−4	−7
−3	3	0	−2	−3	−4	−6	−9
−6	0	−3	−5	−6	−7	−9	−12

Exercise 55 *page 57*

1. 8	2. 15	3. 16	4. −8	5. −14
6. −4	7. −15	8. −10	9. −11	10. −14
11. −16	12. −7	13. −15	14. −6x	15. −11y
16. −8z	17. −6a	18. −13b	19 −14c	20. −13d

Exercise 56 *page 58*

1. 6	2. 4	3. 5	4. 15	5. 4x
6. 8y	7. 8z	8. 4	9. 2	10. 6
11. 6a	12. 4b	13. 3c	14. −3	15. −6
16. −8	17. −6	18. −4p	19. −7q	20. −r
21. −2	22. −5	23. −7	24. −4u	25. −3v

Exercise 57 *page 58*

1.

take → from ↓	4	3	2	1	0	−1	−2
6	2	3	4	5	6	7	8
3	−1	0	1	2	3	4	5
0	−4	−3	−2	−1	0	1	2
−3	−7	−6	−5	−4	−3	−2	−1

2.

take → from ↓	6	4	2	0	−2	−4	−6
12	6	8	10	12	14	16	18
6	0	2	4	6	8	10	12
0	−6	−4	−2	0	2	4	6
−3	−12	−10	−8	−6	−4	−2	0

3.

take → / from ↓	12	9	6	3	0	−3	−6
12	0	3	6	9	12	15	18
6	−6	−3	0	3	6	9	12
0	−12	−9	−6	−3	0	3	6
−6	−18	−15	−12	−9	−6	−3	0

4.

take → / from ↓	4	3	2	1	0	−1	−2
4	0	1	2	3	4	5	6
0	−4	−3	−2	−1	0	1	2
−4	−8	−7	−6	−5	−4	−3	−2
−8	−12	−11	−10	−9	−8	−7	−6

5.

take → / from ↓	4	3	2	1	0	−1	−2
2	−2	−1	0	1	2	3	4
0	−4	−3	−2	−1	0	1	2
−2	−6	−5	−4	−3	−2	−1	0
−4	−8	−7	−6	−5	−4	−3	−2

6.

take → / from ↓	15	10	5	0	−5	−10	−15
10	−5	0	5	10	15	20	25
5	−10	−5	0	5	10	15	20
0	−15	−10	−5	0	5	10	15
−5	−20	−15	−10	−5	0	5	10

Exercise 58   *page 59*

1. 4　　　2. 7　　　3. $2x$　　　4. $6y$　　　5. −2
6. −5　　　7. $-5z$　　　8. $-6t$　　　9. $-2u$　　　10. $-v$
11. −5　　　12. −15　　　13. −14　　　14. $-11p$　　　15. $-10q$
16. −9　　　17. −17　　　18. $-13a$　　　19. $-15b$　　　20. $-16c$

Exercise 59   *page 59*

1. 7　　　2. 12　　　3. $11x$　　　4. $12y$　　　5. 10
6. 15　　　7. $10z$　　　8. $18t$　　　9. 4　　　10. 1
11. 3　　　12. 7　　　13. $5a$　　　14. $2b$　　　15. $8c$
16. d　　　17. −3　　　18. −2　　　19. −5　　　20. $-6x$
21. $-6y$　　　22. $-4z$　　　23. $-5t$　　　24. $-4u$　　　25. $-v$

Exercise 60   *page 60*

1.

×	10	5	0	−5	−10
10	100	50	0	−50	−100
5	50	25	0	−25	−50
0	0	0	0	0	0
−5	−50	−25	0	25	50
−10	−100	−50	0	50	100

2.

×	6	3	0	−3	−6
6	36	18	0	−18	−36
3	18	9	0	−9	−18
0	0	0	0	0	0
−3	−18	−9	0	9	18
−6	−36	−18	0	18	36

3.

X	4	2	0	−2	−4
8	32	16	0	−16	−32
4	16	8	0	−8	−16
0	0	0	0	0	0
−4	−16	−8	0	8	16
−8	−32	−16	0	16	32

4.

X	8	4	0	−4	−8
6	48	24	0	−24	−48
3	24	12	0	−12	−24
0	0	0	0	0	0
−3	−24	−12	0	12	24
−6	−48	−24	0	24	48

5.

X	5	2	0	−2	−5
5	25	10	0	−10	−25
2	10	4	0	−4	−10
0	0	0	0	0	0
−2	−10	−4	0	4	10
−5	−25	−10	0	10	25

6.

X	−1	−2	−3	−4	−5
−1	1	2	3	4	5
0	0	0	0	0	0
1	−1	−2	−3	−4	−5
2	−2	−4	−6	−8	−10
3	−3	−6	−9	−12	−15

Exercise 61   *page 61*

1. 60	2. 8	3. 18	4. 30	5. 32
6. 42	7. 36	8. 8	9. 12	10. 4
11. 16	12. 24	13. −15	14. −32	15. −54
16. −84	17. −6	18. −20	19. −12	20. −6
21. −8	22. −24	23. −35	24. −72	25. −33
26. −10	27. −35	28. −20	29. −15	30. −12
31. $6a$	32. $20ab$	33. $30a^2$	34. $15x$	35. $28y$
36. $72z$	37. $8a$	38. $35b$	39. $15mn$	40. $40pq$
41. $28x^2$	42. $27y^2$	43. $−21x$	44. $−45y$	45. $−44z$
46. $−24a$	47. $−36b$	48. $−42uv$	49. $−60pq$	50. $−32m^2$
51. $−63n^2$	52. $−36p$	53. $−35q$	54. $−70r$	55. $−18a$
56. $−108b$	57. $−56xy$	58. $−55mn$	59. $−72t^2$	60. $−12u^2$

Exercise 62   *page 61*

1. 5	2. 4	3. 4	4. 3	5. 4
6. 7	7. 16	8. 14	9. 9	10. 4
11. 6	12. −5	13. −4	14. −8	15. −7
16. −15	17. −12	18. −9	19. −9	20. −3
21. −3	22. −5	23. −9	24. −9	25. −14
26. −13	27. −75	28. $−4\frac{1}{2}$	29. $−3\frac{1}{2}$	30. $−2\frac{1}{2}$
31. 5	32. 4	33. $6a$	34. $3a$	35. $9x$
36. $5y$	37. $4z$	38. 7	39. 5	40. 9
41. 8	42. 9	43. 7	44. $−4x$	45. $−8y$
46. −6	47. −6	48. −4	49. −6	50. −5

51. −6	**52.** −3	**53.** −8a	**54.** −3b	**55.** −3	
56. −4	**57.** −7	**58.** −7s	**59.** −12c	**60.** −10d	

Exercise 63 *page 62*

1. 6	**2.** 2	**3.** 8	**4.** 28	**5.** 8	**6.** 20
7. 8	**8.** 8	**9.** 16	**10.** 4	**11.** 16	**12.** 32
13. 10	**14.** 8	**15.** 14	**16.** 0	**17.** 12	**18.** 4
19. 20	**20.** 32	**21.** 12	**22.** 32	**23.** 16	**24.** 64
25. 8	**26.** 2	**27.** 20	**28.** 15	**29.** 11	**30.** 17
31. 15	**32.** 30	**33.** 75	**34.** 25	**35.** 9	**36.** 45
37. 19	**38.** 9	**39.** 16	**40.** 75	**41.** 45	**42.** 125
43. 27	**44.** 54	**45.** 59	**46.** 100	**47.** 225	**48.** 450

Exercise 64 *page 62*

1. 9	**2.** 4	**3.** 5	**4.** −8	**5.** −5	**6.** −9
7. −8	**8.** −10	**9.** −8	**10.** 10	**11.** 2	**12.** 1
13. −18	**14.** −5	**15.** −4	**16.** −45	**17.** −14	**18.** −21
19. 14	**20.** 9	**21.** 8	**22.** −15	**23.** 5	**24.** 11
25. −16	**26.** −2	**27.** −9	**28.** 18	**29.** 12	**30.** 14
31. −16	**32.** 5	**33.** 6	**34.** −60	**35.** −4	**36.** −5

Exercise 65 *page 63*

1. 7	**2.** 3	**3.** 4	**4.** −6	**5.** −6	**6.** −4
7. −8	**8.** −6	**9.** −8	**10.** −12	**11.** −20	**12.** −9
13. −9	**14.** −7	**15.** −5	**16.** −9	**17.** −9	**18.** −8
19. −9	**20.** −6	**21.** −5	**22.** 5	**23.** 4	**24.** 5
25. 6	**26.** 20	**27.** 5	**28.** 4	**29.** 8	**30.** 12

Exercise 66 *page 63*

1. −6	**2.** −12	**3.** 8	**4.** 0	**5.** 0	**6.** −12
7. 32	**8.** 0	**9.** 0	**10.** −36	**11.** 24	**12.** 0
13. 0	**14.** 0	**15.** 0	**16.** 48	**17.** 120	**18.** 0
19. 0	**20.** 0	**21.** 6	**22.** 12	**23.** 2	**24.** 18
25. 3	**26.** 6	**27.** 12	**28.** 54	**29.** 24	**30.** 10
31. −36	**32.** −18	**33.** −12	**34.** −6	**35.** 36	**36.** −36
37. −72	**38.** −24	**39.** 24	**40.** 180		

Exercise 67 *page 64*

1. 4	**2.** 80	**3.** −8	**4.** −16	**5.** −32	**6.** 64
7. 36	**8.** 6	**9.** −54	**10.** −27	**11.** −12	**12.** 45
13. 45	**14.** 12	**15.** −32	**16.** −36	**17.** 60	**18.** 72
19. 32	**20.** 54	**21.** −81	**22.** −48	**23.** 72	**24.** 144
25. 28	**26.** 99	**27.** −40	**28.** 36	**29.** −36	**30.** 108

Revision exercise D
page 64

1. (b)	**2.** (a)	**3.** (a)	**4.** (b)	**5.** (a)	**6.** (c)
7. (a)	**8.** (b)	**9.** (b)	**10.** (c)	**11.** (a)	**12.** (a)
13. (c)	**14.** (b)	**15.** (b)	**16.** (a)	**17.** (c)	**18.** (b)
19. (a)	**20.** (b)	**21.** 14	**22.** 12	**23.** 18	**24.** 22
25. 18	**26.** 40	**27.** 72	**28.** 112	**29.** 32	**30.** 20
31. 32	**32.** 128	**33.** 16	**34.** 96	**35.** 64	**36.** 8
37. 72	**38.** 128	**39.** 16	**40.** 40	**41.** 7	**42.** 16
43. 3	**44.** 5	**45.** 60	**46.** 105	**47.** 150	**48.** 45
49. 16	**50.** 75	**51.** 150	**52.** 450	**53.** 45	**54.** 180
55. 125	**56.** 27	**57.** 98	**58.** 250	**59.** 108	**60.** 270
61. −18	**62.** 32	**63.** −60	**64.** −6	**65.** −6	**66.** 3
67. −2	**68.** −12	**69.** 20	**70.** 6	**71.** 12	**72.** 16
73. 48	**74.** 0	**75.** 0	**76.** 12	**77.** 72	**78.** 60
79. 6	**80.** 6	**81.** 12	**82.** 12	**83.** 36	**84.** 30

85. −9   86. −2   87. −3   88. −108   89. 0   90. 0
91. (a) 144 cm², 60 cm   (b) 144 cm², 52 cm
    (c) 144 cm², 50 cm   (d) 144 cm², 48 cm
92. (a) 6 m², 12 m   (b) 30 m², 30 m   (c) 60 cm², 40 cm
    (d) 84 cm², 56 cm   (e) 210 mm², 70 mm

BOOK 3   PART 6

Exercise 70 *page 73*

1. A ∩ B = { 2, 3, 4, 5, 6 }
   A ∪ B = { 1, 2, 3, 4, 5, 6, 7, 8, 9, 10 }
2. A ∩ B = { 3, 5, 7 }
   A ∪ B = { 1, 2, 3, 5, 7, 9 }
3. A ∩ B = { Sunday }
   A ∪ B = { Monday, Friday, Saturday, Sunday }
4. A ∩ B = { Thursday }
   A ∪ B = { Tuesday, Thursday, Saturday }
5. A ∩ B = { Arctic }
   A ∪ B = { Atlantic, Arctic, Indian }
6. A ∩ B = { 1, 3, 5 }
   A ∪ B = { 1, 2, 3, 5, 6, 10 }
7. A ∩ B = { 1, 3, 9 }
   A ∪ B = { 1, 2, 3, 6, 9 }
8. A ∩ B = φ
   A ∪ B = { 1, 4, 5, 9, 10 }
9. A ∩ B = φ
   A ∪ B = { 1, 3, 4, 6, 8, 10 }
10. A ∩ B = { 1, 2, 3, 6 }
    A ∩ C = { 1, 2, 4 }
    B ∩ C = { 1, 2, 5, 10 }
    A ∩ B ∩ C = { 1, 2 }
11. A ∩ B = { 1, 2, 4 }
    A ∩ B ∩ C = { 1, 2 }
    B ∩ C = { 1, 2, 3, 6 }
    A ∩ C = { 1, 2 }
12. A ∩ B = { 6, 12 }
    A ∩ C = { 4, 8, 12 }
    B ∩ C = { 12 }
    A ∩ B ∩ C = { 12 }
13. A ∩ B = φ
    A ∩ C = { Africa }
    B ∩ C = { America }
    A ∩ B ∩ C = φ
14. ℰ = { numbers from 1 to 12 }
    A = { multiples of 2 }   B = { multiples of 3 }
15. ℰ = { seasons of the year }
    A = { seasons whose names begin with S }
    B = { seasons whose names end with R }
16. ℰ = { units of money }   A = { silver coins }
    B = { copper coins }
17. ℰ = { months of the year }
    A = { months whose names begin with J }
    B = { months whose names end with Y }
18. ℰ = { months of the year }   A = { months with 31 days }
    B = { months whose names begin with M }

19. $\mathscr{E} = \{$ numbers from 1 to 10 $\}$ $A = \{$ square numbers $\}$
    $B = \{$ triangular numbers $\}$ $C = \{$ odd numbers $\}$
20. $\mathscr{E} = \{$ numbers from 1 to 10 $\}$ $A = \{$ triangular numbers $\}$
    $B = \{$ even numbers $\}$ $C = \{$ prime numbers $\}$

Exercise 71   *page 75*

1. (a) $A' = \{1, 4, 6, 8, 9, 10\}$ (b) $B' = \{2, 4, 6, 8, 10\}$
   (c) $A' \cap B' = \{4, 6, 8, 10\}$ (d) $A' \cup B' = \{1, 2, 4, 6, 8, 9, 10\}$
2. (a) $A' = \{2, 4, 5, 7, 8, 9\}$ (b) $B' = \{1, 3, 5, 7, 9\}$
   (c) $A' \cap B' = \{5, 7, 9\}$ (d) $A' \cup B' = \{1, 2, 3, 4, 5, 7, 8, 9\}$
3. (a) $A' = \{2, 4, 5, 7, 8, 9\}$ (b) $B' = \{1, 2, 4, 5, 7, 8, 10\}$
   (c) $A' \cap B' = \{2, 4, 5, 7, 8\}$ (d) $A' \cup B' = \{1, 2, 4, 5, 7, 8, 9, 10\}$
4. (a) $A' = \{2, 4, 5, 7, 8, 9\}$ (b) $B' = \{3, 4, 6, 7, 8, 9\}$
   (c) $A' \cap B' = \{4, 7, 8, 9\}$ (d) $A' \cup B' = \{2, 3, 4, 5, 6, 7, 8, 9\}$
5. (a) $A' = \{2, 3, 5, 6, 7, 8, 10\}$ (b) $B' = \{2, 4, 6, 8, 10\}$
   (c) $A' \cap B' = \{2, 6, 8, 10\}$ (d) $A' \cup B' = \{2, 3, 4, 5, 6, 7, 8, 10\}$
6. (a) $A' = \{2, 3, 5, 6, 7, 8, 10\}$ (b) $B' = \{1, 2, 4, 5, 7, 8, 10\}$
   (c) $A' \cap B' = \{2, 5, 7, 8, 10\}$ (d) $A' \cup B' = \{1, 2, 3, 4, 5, 6, 7, 8, 10\}$
7. (a) $A' = \{$ Manchester City, Everton, Leeds United $\}$
   (b) $B' = \{$ Manchester City, Liverpool, Everton, Arsenal,
         Nottingham Forest $\}$
   (c) $A' \cap B' = \{$ Manchester City, Everton $\}$
   (d) $A' \cup B' = \{$ Manchester City, Liverpool, Everton, Leeds United, Arsenal,
         Nottingham Forest $\}$
8. (a) $A' = \{$ Birmingham City, Middlesbrough, Tottenham Hotspur $\}$
   (b) $B' = \{$ West Bromwich Albion, Newcastle United, Sunderland,
         Middlesbrough, Tottenham Hotspur $\}$
   (c) $A' \cap B' = \{$ Middlesbrough, Tottenham Hotspur $\}$
   (d) $A' \cup B' = \{$ Birmingham City, Middlesbrough, Tottenham Hotspur,
         West Bromwich Albion, Newcastle United, Sunderland $\}$
9. (a) $A' = \{$ Leicester, Leeds $\}$
   (b) $B' = \{$ London, Leeds $\}$
   (c) $A' \cap B' = \{$ Leeds $\}$
   (d) $A' \cup B' = \{$ London, Leeds, Leicester $\}$
10. (a) $A' = \{$ red, green, blue $\}$
    (b) $B' = \{$ red, yellow, green, indigo, violet $\}$
    (c) $A' \cap B' = \{$ red, green $\}$
    (d) $A' \cup B' = \{$ red, yellow, green, blue, indigo, violet $\}$
11. (a) $A' = \{$ willow, birch $\}$
    (b) $B' = \{$ oak, elm, willow $\}$
    (c) $A' \cap B' = \{$ willow $\}$
    (d) $A' \cup B' = \{$ oak, elm, willow, birch $\}$
12. (a) $A' = \{$ bluebell, rose $\}$
    (b) $B' = \{$ bluebell, tulip $\}$

(c) A′ ∩ B′ = { bluebell }
(d) A′ ∪ B′ = { bluebell, rose, tulip }
13. (a) A′ = { netball, hockey }
    (b) B′ = { football, hockey }
    (c) A′ ∩ B′ = { hockey }
    (d) A′ ∪ B′ = { netball, football, hockey }
14. (a) A′ = { snooker, billiards, golf }
    (b) B′ = { cricket, rounders, golf }
    (c) A′ ∩ B′ = { golf }
    (d) A′ ∪ B′ = { cricket, snooker, billiards, rounders, golf }
15. (a) A′ = { parallelogram }
    (b) B′ = { rectangle, parallelogram }
    (c) A′ ∩ B′ = { parallelogram }
    (d) A′ ∪ B′ = { parallelogram, rectangle }

Exercise 72   *page 77*

Arsenal	30	Leeds United	29
Tottenham Hotspur	29	Aston Villa	27
Nottingham Forest	26	Southampton	26
Coventry City	26	Everton	26
Newcastle United	24	West Ham United	24
Ipswich Town	24	West Bromwich Albion	23
Wolverhampton Wanderers	22	Manchester City	22
Stoke City	21	Birmingham City	21
Sunderland	21	Derby County	20
Bristol City	20	Leicester City	20

Exercise 73   *page 77*

1. 26   2. 38   3. 29   4. 50   5. 39   6. 48
7. 19   8. 44   9. 34   10. 56   11. 58   12. 45
13. 57   14. 42   15. 47   16. 47   17. 48   18. 17
19. not possible   20. not possible   21. not possible
22. 0   23. 4   24. 4   25. 10   26. 10   27. 12
28. 12   29. 30   30. 30

Exercise 74   *page 78*

1. $\begin{pmatrix} 30 \\ 23 \\ 12 \end{pmatrix}$ 2. $\begin{pmatrix} 53 \\ 33 \\ 18 \end{pmatrix}$ 3. $\begin{pmatrix} 37 \\ 21 \\ 13 \end{pmatrix}$ 4. $\begin{pmatrix} 38 \\ 25 \\ 8 \end{pmatrix}$ 5. $\begin{pmatrix} 32 \\ 19 \\ 11 \end{pmatrix}$ 6. $\begin{pmatrix} 32 \\ 24 \\ 12 \end{pmatrix}$

7. $\begin{pmatrix} 92 \\ 56 \end{pmatrix}$ 8. $\begin{pmatrix} 84 \\ 57 \end{pmatrix}$ 9. $\begin{pmatrix} 80 \\ 58 \end{pmatrix}$ 10. $\begin{pmatrix} 200 \\ 110 \end{pmatrix}$ 11. $\begin{pmatrix} 300 \\ 150 \end{pmatrix}$ 12. $\begin{pmatrix} 350 \\ 70 \end{pmatrix}$

Exercise 75   *page 79*

1. England   15   All Blacks 26
2. Ireland   12   All Blacks 29
3. Scotland   9   All Blacks 15
4. Wales   19   All Blacks 19
5. France   24   All Blacks 21

Exercise 76   *page 80*

1. $\begin{pmatrix} 13 & 21 \\ 21 & 27 \end{pmatrix}$ 2. $\begin{pmatrix} 20 & 26 \\ 14 & 18 \end{pmatrix}$ 3. $\begin{pmatrix} 13 & 16 \\ 22 & 16 \end{pmatrix}$ 4. $\begin{pmatrix} 19 & 11 \\ 14 & 7 \end{pmatrix}$ 5. $\begin{pmatrix} 26 & 13 \\ 26 & 13 \end{pmatrix}$

6. $\begin{pmatrix} 26 & 8 \\ 31 & 7 \end{pmatrix}$ 7. $\begin{pmatrix} 15 & 6 \\ 20 & 8 \end{pmatrix}$ 8. $\begin{pmatrix} 15 & 10 \\ 9 & 6 \end{pmatrix}$ 9. $\begin{pmatrix} 13 & 8 \\ 8 & 5 \end{pmatrix}$ 10. $\begin{pmatrix} 8 & 5 \\ 13 & 8 \end{pmatrix}$

11. $\begin{pmatrix} 12 & 7 \\ 7 & 4 \end{pmatrix}$ 12. $\begin{pmatrix} 8 & 13 \\ 5 & 8 \end{pmatrix}$ 13. $\begin{pmatrix} 13 & 11 \\ 15 & 15 \end{pmatrix}$ 14. $\begin{pmatrix} 13 & 10 \\ 17 & 13 \end{pmatrix}$ 15. $\begin{pmatrix} 10 & 11 \\ 25 & 9 \end{pmatrix}$

16. $\begin{pmatrix} 7 & 19 \\ 10 & 11 \end{pmatrix}$ 17. $\begin{pmatrix} 12 & 9 \\ 8 & 6 \end{pmatrix}$ 18. $\begin{pmatrix} 20 & 5 \\ 24 & 6 \end{pmatrix}$ 19. $\begin{pmatrix} 22 & 11 \\ 16 & 13 \end{pmatrix}$ 20. $\begin{pmatrix} 20 & 10 \\ 17 & 3 \end{pmatrix}$

21. $\begin{pmatrix} 1 & 2 \\ 4 & 3 \end{pmatrix}$ 22. $\begin{pmatrix} 2 & 1 \\ 3 & 4 \end{pmatrix}$ 23. $\begin{pmatrix} 3 & 0 \\ 7 & 0 \end{pmatrix}$ 24. $\begin{pmatrix} 0 & 3 \\ 0 & 7 \end{pmatrix}$ 25. $\begin{pmatrix} 1 & 1 \\ 4 & 4 \end{pmatrix}$

26. $\begin{pmatrix} 2 & 2 \\ 3 & 3 \end{pmatrix}$ 27. $\begin{pmatrix} 0 & 4 \\ 4 & 0 \end{pmatrix}$ 28. $\begin{pmatrix} 0 & 4 \\ 4 & 0 \end{pmatrix}$ 29. $\begin{pmatrix} 9 & 0 \\ 0 & 9 \end{pmatrix}$ 30. $\begin{pmatrix} 9 & 0 \\ 0 & 9 \end{pmatrix}$

Revision exercise E
page 81

1. $\mathscr{E}$ = { hot drinks }
   A = { hot drinks whose names begin with C }
   B = { hot drinks whose names end with A }
2. $\mathscr{E}$ = { planets }
   A = { planets whose names begin with M }
   B = { planets whose names end with S }
3. $\mathscr{E}$ = { the first five square numbers }
   A = { square numbers which are odd }
   B = { square numbers which are even }
4. $\mathscr{E}$ = { the first five triangular numbers }
   A = { triangular numbers which divide by 3 }
   B = { triangular numbers which divide by 5 }
5. $\mathscr{E}$ = { the first ten square numbers }
   A = { square numbers which are even }
   B = { square numbers which divide by 9 }
   C = { square numbers with two digits }
6. $\mathscr{E}$ = { the first five triangular numbers }
   A = { triangular numbers which are even }
   B = { triangular numbers which divide by 3 }
   C = { triangular numbers with one digit }
7. $\mathscr{E}$ = { men on a cricket pitch }
   A = { men on the batting side }
   B = { men on the fielding side }
   C = { men who wear pads }
8. (a) A = { 10, 20, 30 }   (b) B = { 15, 30 }
   (c) A $\cap$ B = { 30 }   (d) A $\cup$ B = { 10, 15, 20, 30 }
   (e) A$'$ = { 5, 15, 25 }   (f) B$'$ = { 5, 10, 20, 25 }
   (g) A$'$ $\cap$ B$'$ = { 5, 25 }   (h) A$'$ $\cup$ B$'$ = { 5, 10, 15, 20, 25 }
9. (a) A = { stars, sun }   (b) B = { sun, moon }
   (c) A $\cap$ B = { sun }   (d) A $\cup$ B = { stars, sun, moon }
   (e) A$'$ = { moon }   (f) B$'$ = { stars }
   (g) A$'$ $\cap$ B$'$ = ϕ (h) A$'$ $\cup$ B$'$ = { moon, stars }
10. £7

answers

Exercise 2 *page 2*   **1.** 232   **2.** 169   **3.** 148   **4.** 259   **5.** 97   **6.** 14   **7.** 10   **8.** 15
9. 25   **10.** 26   **11.** 44   **12.** 34   **13.** 47   **14.** 94   **15.** 38   **16.** 43
17. (b)   **18.** (a)   **19.** (b)   **20.** (c)   **21.** (c)   **22.** (a)   **23.** (a)   **24.** (b)
25. (b)   **26.** (b)

Exercise 3 *page 2*   **1.** 613_{eight} **2.** 556_{eight} **3.** 704_{eight} **4.** 760_{eight}
5. 2241_{five} **6.** 2114_{five} **7.** 1402_{five} **8.** 3000_{five}
9. 100011_{two} **10.** 101010_{two} **11.** 11101_{two} **12.** 10100_{two}
13. 1023_{four} **14.** 1200_{four} **15.** 311_{four} **16.** 1021_{three}
17. 221_{three} **18.** 281_{twelve} **19.** $1E3_{twelve}$ **20.** $12T_{twelve}$

Exercise 4 *page 3*   **1.** 0·375   **2.** 0·3   **3.** 0·7   **4.** 0·4   **5.** 0·8
6. 0·45   **7.** 0·55   **8.** 0·225   **9.** 0·425   **10.** 0·175
11. 0·025   **12.** 0·22   **13.** 0·82   **14.** 0·3125   **15.** 0·5625

Exercise 5 *page 3*   **1.** 0·$\dot6$ **2.** 0·$\dot3$ **3.** 0·8$\dot3$ **4.** 0·1$\dot6$ **5.** 0·41$\dot6$
6. 0·583   **7.** 0·91$\dot6$ **8.** 0·08$\dot3$ **9.** 0·$\dot4$ **10.** 0·$\dot7$
11. 0·$\dot1$ **12.** 0·5$\dot4$ **13.** 0·2$\dot7$ **14.** 0·2$\dot3$ **15.** 0·4$\dot3$

Exercise 6 *page 3*   **1.** (a) 94·8 kg   (b) 66 kg   (c) 16·5 kg   **2.** 200 g
3. 1 litre   **4.** (a) 3·5 m   (b) 2·5 m   (c) 6·4 m²
5. (a) B by 1·3 cm   (b) A by 0·5 m²

Exercise 7 *page 4*   **1.** 3 : 5   **2.** 2 : 5   **3.** 3 : 10   **4.** 2 : 3   **5.** 3 : 5
6. 3 : 4   **7.** 2 : 5   **8.** 1 : 5   **9.** 3 : 8   **10.** 2 : 5
11. 2 : 5   **12.** 3 : 4   **13.** 3 : 4   **14.** 2 : 5   **15.** 3 : 10
16. 1 : 4   **17.** 1 : 8   **18.** 2 : 5   **19.** 5 : 6   **20.** 9 : 10
21. 1 : 5   **22.** 4 : 5   **23.** 3 : 8   **24.** 1 : 5   **25.** 1 : 4

Exercise 8 *page 4*   **1.** £32, £16   **2.** £45, £15   **3.** £64, £16
4. £78, £13   **5.** £42, £28   **6.** £75, £45
7. 64 ml, 48 ml   **8.** 72 ml, 90 ml   **9.** 75 g, 125 g
10. 36 g, 84 g   **11.** £54, £36, £18   **12.** £80, £48, £16
13. £60, £45, £30   **14.** £90, £75, £15   **15.** £120, £100, £80
16. 180 g, 90 g, 45 g   **17.** 120 kg, 150 kg, 180 kg
18. 300 m*l*, 450 m*l*, 750 m*l*   **19.** 120 m*l*, 200 m*l*, 240 m*l*
20. 12, 18 and 20

Exercise 9   *page 5*

1. 45p
2. 40p
3. 45p, 81p
4. £28, £40
5. £32, £52
6. £15, £25
7. £15, £21
8. 30p, 45p, £1
9. 36p
10. 150 cm
11. 60 kg
12. 250 m*l*, 400 m*l*
13. 14, 26
14. 55 cm, 1 m
15. 150 g, 200 g, 450 g
16. 10, 16, 30
17. 8, 14, 28
18. 18p
19. £8, £36
20. 8 years

Exercise 10   *page 6*

1. 54p
2. 64p
3. £1·50
4. 81 min, 36 min
5. £25, £40
6. 96p
7. £2·70
8. £1·28, £1·60
9. £1·08, £1·44
10. £1·20, £3·20
11. £5·60, £16·80
12. £1·50, £3·50
13. £3·60, £9·60, £14·40
14. £22·50, £30, £90
15. £2·40, £3·60, £9
16. 5
17. 3
18. 15
19. 3, 8
20. 2, 7
21. 4, 9
22. 4, 10
23. 5, 8
24. 25, 45
25. 3, 10
26. 3, 7
27. 4, 7, 9
28. 3, 8, 14
29. 15, 50
30. 8, 20

Exercise 11   *page 7*

1. £40
2. £45
3. 24 g
4. £36
5. £12
6. £54
7. 15 cm
8. £48
9. £88
10. £10
11. £9
12. 15 cm
13. 28 cm
14. £24
15. £21
16. £48
17. £21
18. 36 cm
19. 18 g
20. 60p
21. 72p
22. 88 cm
23. 70p
24. £1·50
25. £1·28
26. 45p
27. 90 cm
28. 750 g
29. £9
30. 60p

Exercise 12   *page 8*

1. 9%
2. 7%
3. 8%
4. 6%
5. 70%
6. 30%
7. 90%
8. 40%
9. 80%
10. 60%
11. 40%
12. 80%
13. 20%
14. 35%
15. 55%
16. 15%
17. 45%
18. 75%
19. 25%
20. 80%
21. 40%
22. 60%
23. 80%
24. 40%
25. 80%
26. 60%
27. 20%
28. 25%
29. 75%
30. $12\frac{1}{2}$%

Exercise 13   *page 8*

1. 15
2. 36 min
3. 27 m^2
4. 14
5. 27
6. 4
7. 140
8. 15
9. 5, 7, 8
10. 60, 75, 45, 15, 30
11. 30%
12. 80%
13. 70%
14. 75%
15. 45%
16. 75%
17. 90%
18. 80%
19. 40%, 30%, 10%, 20%
20. 6%, 4%, 10%, 8%, 12%

Exercise 14   *page 9*

1. 10 min
2. 51 min
3. 54 s
4. 2 min 7 s
5. 1 h 7 min
6. 4 h 13 min
7. 30 days
8. 1 year 7 months
9. 1 h 30 min
10. 2 h 34 min
11. 4 min 13 s
12. 1 h 42 min

Exercise 15   *page 10*

1. 1950
2. 1715
3. 30
4. 600
5. 480 km
6. yes
7. 102
8. 36
9. 40
10. £2·70
11. £15
12. £8·10
13. £121·80
14. 7 h 30 min
15. 4 h 30 min

Exercise 16   *page 11*

1. 8
2. 6
3. 5
4. 18
5. 10 weeks
6. 12
7. 1 year 4 months
8. 150
9. 5 years
10. 10
11. 5
12. 20

Revision exercise A
page 11

1. (b)	2. (c)	3. (a)	4. (a)	5. (b)
6. (c)	7. (a)	8. (b)	9. (b)	10. (a)
11. (a)	12. (b)	13. (c)	14. (a)	15. (b)
16. (b)	17. (c)	18. (a)	19. (a)	20. (b)

21. (a) 4   (b) 2   (c) 14   (d) 8
22. (a) 20   (b) £3   (c) 15p
23. (a) 20, 12, 16, 20, 12   (b) 80   (c) 25%, 15%, 20%, 25%, 15%
24. (a) 30, 36, 24, 30   (b) 120   (c) 25%, 30%, 20%, 25%
    (d) 24, 28, 26, 22, 20   (e) 24
25. (b) boys, 60%, 50%, 70%, 40%, 75%
       girls, 45%, 80%, 55%, 35%, 65%
26. (a) 7   (b) 70 cm   (c) 10%

BOOK 4   PART 2

Exercise 17   *page 14*

2. (a) equal   (b) equal   (c) supplementary
   (d) supplementary   (e) equal
3. (b), (e), (d), (c), (a)

Exercise 18   *page 15*

1. $50°, 60°$ 2. $70°, 130°$ 3. $80°, 140°$
4. $40°, 70°$ 5. $60°, 110°$ 6. $50°, 150°$
7. $110°, 150°$ 8. $140°, 60°$ 9. $100°, 50°$
10. $60°, 60°, 120°, 45°, 45°, 135°$
11. $55°, 55°, 125°, 95°, 95°, 85°$
12. $75°, 75°, 105°, 145°, 145°, 35°$

Exercise 19   *page 16*

1. Yes	2. Yes	3. No	4. Yes	5. No
6. No	7. Yes	8. No	9. Yes	10. No

Exercise 23   *page 19*

1. (a) 5   (b) 8   (c) 9   (d) 10   (e) 12
2. (a) 2, 3   (b) 5, 6   (c) 6, 7   (d) 7, 8   (e) 9, 10
3. (a) $540°$ (b) $1080°$ (c) $1260°$ (d) $1440°$ (e) $1800°$
4. (a) $108°$ (b) $135°$ (c) $140°$ (d) $144°$ (e) $150°$

Exercise 24   *page 20*

1. (a) 5   (b) 6   (c) 9   (d) 10   (e) 12
2. $360°$ in all cases
3. (a) $72°$ (b) $60°$ (c) $40°$ (d) $36°$ (e) $30°$
4. $180°$ in all cases

Exercise 25   *page 21*

1. isosceles triangle, isosceles trapezium
2. isosceles triangle, kite, kite
3. square, rectangle, kite, isosceles trapezium, isosceles triangle (right-angled), isosceles triangle (right-angled), isosceles triangle
4. isosceles triangle, isosceles trapezium, isosceles trapezium
5. regular nonagon, equilateral triangle, isosceles trapezium
6. regular pentagon, regular pentagon, rhombus, isosceles trapezium, kite
7. regular hexagon, equilateral triangle, rhombus, isosceles trapezium
8. square, regular octagon

Exercise 26 *page 24*

1. (a), (b) and (d) 2. (a) and (d) 3. (b), (c) and (d)
4. (a), (b) and (c) 5. (a), (b), (c) and (d) 6. (a) and (c)
7. (b) and (c) 8. (b) and (d) 9. (b), (c) and (d)
10. (a), (b) and (d) 11. (a) and (d) 12. (a), (b), (c) and (d)
13. (b) and (d) 14. (a), (b) and (d) 15. (a), (b), (c) and (d)

Exercise 28 *page 30*

1. ADM and BCN
2. ACX and ABX
3. BPQ and DSR
4. ABF and DCE, BCF and ECF
5. AWZ and CYX, BWX and DYZ
6. AKN and BKL, DMN and CML
7. AED and ABC, ADM and ACM
8. ADE and CDE, ADB and CDB, AEB and CEB
9. ABC and EFG, ACH and EGD, CHD and GDH
10. AXC and BXD, ABC and ABD, ACD and BCD

Exercise 29 *page 32*

1. $75°, 60°, 45°$ 2. $55°, 60°, 65°$ 3. $110°, 25°, 45°$
4. $50°, 65°, 65°$ 5. $100°, 40°, 40°$ 6. $130°, 25°, 25°$
7. $90°, 30°, 60°$ 8. $90°, 25°, 65°$ 9. 9 cm
10. 2 cm 11. 4 cm 12. $4\frac{1}{2}$ cm
13. 2 cm 14. 5 cm 15. 7 cm

Exercise 30 *page 33*

1. 7 cm, $10\frac{1}{2}$ cm 2. 10 cm, $16\frac{1}{2}$ cm 3. 8 cm, 14 cm
4. 10 cm, $17\frac{1}{2}$ cm 5. 5 cm, $11\frac{1}{2}$ cm 6. 8 cm, 8 cm
7. 10 cm, 10 cm 8. 7 cm, 7 cm

Revision exercise B
page 33

1. (a) regular hexagon (b) $120°, 60°, 60°$ (c) $360°$
2. (a) regular pentagon (b) $108°, 72°, 36°$ (c) $180°$
3. $160°, 40°$ 4. $110°, 110°, 40°$

BOOK 4   PART 3

Exercise 31 *page 35*

1. (a) 60 cm, 140 cm, 180 cm, 220 cm
   (b) sixth, eighth, twelfth, fourteenth
2. (a) 11 cm, 15 cm, 18 cm 21 cm
   (b) 20 g, 35 g, 50 g
3. (a) 4 mm, 12 mm, 32 mm (b) 200, 300, 450
4. (a) 200 g, 800 g, 1200 g (b) 150, 400, 450
5. (a) 150, 168 (b) 480 g
6. (a) BF 30, BF 120, BF 210, BF 450
   (b) £2.50, £4, £6.50
7. 90p, £1.08, £1.44 8. 210 cm, 162 cm
9. (a) 65 mm, 80 mm (b) 150 cm, 170 cm
10. 40%, 55%, 70%, 3, 5, 16

Exercise 32 *page 38*

1. $x = 5$ 2. $x = 3$ 3. $x = 6$ 4. $y = 2$ 5. $y = 5$
6. $y = 1$ 7. $y = 0$ 8. $x + y = 4$ 9. $x + y = 6$ 10. $y = \frac{1}{2}x$

Exercise 33 *page 41*   1. $x > 3$ 2. $y > 4$ 3. $x + y > 5$ 4. $x + y \geqslant 3$ 5. $y \geqslant 2x$

6. $x < 4$ 7. $y < 5$ 8. $y \leqslant 3$ 9. $x + y \leqslant 2$ 10. $y \leqslant \frac{1}{2}x$

Revision exercise C
page 42

1.
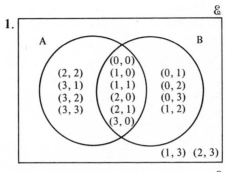

2.
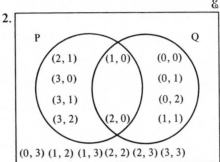

BOOK 4   PART 4

Exercise 35 *page 43*
1. 66 cm   2. 110 cm   3. 154 cm   4. 198 cm
5. 242 mm   6. 440 mm   7. 220 cm   8. 88 cm
9. 132 cm   10. 176 cm   11. 264 mm   12. 660 mm
13. 28·26 cm   14. 62·8 mm   15. 37·68 mm   16. 25·12 cm
17. 21·98 cm   18. 15·7 cm

Exercise 36 *page 44*
1. 12·56 cm²   2. 50·24 cm²   3. 28.26 cm²   4. 78.5 cm²
5. 0·0314 m²   6. 0·12568 m²   7. 0·7855 m²   8. 0·28278 m²
9. 0·50272 m²   10. 314·2 mm²   11. 2790 mm²   12. 1240 mm²
13. 25 110 mm²   14. 11 160 mm²   15. 15 400 mm²   16. 38·5 cm²
17. 616 cm²   18. 1386 cm²   19. 1·54 m²   20. 6·16 m²

Exercise 37 *page 44*
1. 2200 cm, 22 m   2. 785 m   3. 15
4. 5   5. 78·5 mm²   6. 2464 cm²

Exercise 38 *page 45*
1. hexagonal   2. octagonal   3. pentagonal   4. square
5. cube   6. rhomboid   7. trapezoid   8. square

Exercise 39 *page 47*
1. 72 cm³   2. 270 cm³   3. 90 cm³   4. 80 cm³
5. 1000 mm³   6. 480 mm³   7. 12 m³   8. 50 cm³

9. 240 cm^3 10. 105 cm^3 11. 96 cm^3 12. 144 cm^3
13. 360 mm^3 14. 240 mm^3 15. 3080 mm^3 16. 462 cm^3
17. 628 cm^3 18. 251·2 cm^3 19. 198 cm^3 20. 11 000 mm^3

Exercise 40 *page 48*   1. 55 cm^3 2. 180 cm^3 3. 128 cm^3 4. 95 cm^3
5. 44 cm^3 6. 96 cm^3 7. 144 cm^3 8. 480 cm^3

Exercise 41 *page 50*   1. 30   2. 24   3. 36   4. 24   5. 80   6. 125

Exercise 42 *page 50*   1. 12 000 *l*   2. 25 000 *l*   3. 12 *l*   4. 36 *l*
5. 60 *l*   6. 11 *l*   7. 198 000 *l*   8. 314 000 *l*
9. (a) 840 *l*   (b) 10 weeks   10. (a) 27 *l*   (b) 135
11. (a) 308 *l*   (b) 11   12. (a) 44 *l*   (b) 200

Revision exercise D   1. (b)   2. (c)   3. (a)
page 51

BOOK 4   PART 5

Exercise 43 *page 52*   1. 9*a*   2. 11*b*   3. 10*c*   4. 3*d*
5. 4*m*   6. *n*   7. 3*p*   8. 3*q*
9. 6*r*   10. *s*   11. 5*x* + 7*y*   12. 9*u* + 2*v*
13. 4*a* + 5*b*   14. 2*c* + 3*d*   15. 8*m* + 4*n*   16. 2*z* + 7*z*^{2}
17. 5*t* + 8*t*^{2} 18. 9*a* + 7*b*   19. 12*c* + 7*d*   20. 11*m* + 8*n*
21. 7*p* + 5*q*   22. 8*u* + 3*v*   23. 12*x* + *y*   24. 6*a* + 5*b*
25. 3*c* + 7*d*   26. 2*z*^{2} + 5*z*   27. 10*t*^{2} + *t*   28. 3*a* − 2*b*
29. 5*c* − 4*d*   30. 2*m* − 3*n*   31. 10*z*^{2} − 5*z*   32. 7*t*^{2} − 4*t*
33. 3*p* − 2*q*   34. 4*r* − *s*   35. *u* − *v*   36. 5*b* − 2*a*
37. 4*d* − 4*c*   38. 4*y* − 3*x*   39. 5*v* − 2*u*   40. 3*z* − 4*z*^{2}
41. 4*t* − *t*^{2} 42. *n* − *m*   43. 3*p* − 7*q*   44. 5*x* − 8*y*
45. 5*a* − 12*b*   46. 11*c* − 10*d*   47. 2*m* − 9*n*   48. *p* − 10*q*
49. 7*ab*   50. 5*cd*   51. 3*mn*   52. *rs*
53. 2*xy*   54. 5*uv*   55. 5*mn*   56. 7*xy*
57. 7*pq*   58. 6*uv*   59. 2*ab*   60. 0

Exercise 44 *page 52*   1. 4*x* + 8   2. 5*y* + 15   3. 3*z* + 12   4. 6*a* + 6*b*
5. 2*p* − 6   6. 4*q* − 8   7. 3*r* − 3   8. 5*c* − 5*d*
9. 12 − 3*a*   10. 10 − 5*b*   11. 12 − 4*c*   12. 2*v* − 2*u*
13. −3*m* − 6   14. −4*n* − 20   15. −6*p* − 6*q*   16. 6*x* + 4*y*
17. 8*m* + 20*n*   18. 15*p* + 5*q*   19. 3*u* + 12*v*   20. 12*a* − 16*b*
21. 15*c* − 6*d*   22. 12*m* − 6*n*   23. 5*x* − 25*y*   24. 9*q* − 6*p*
25. 16*s* − 20*r*   26. 8*v* − 24*u*   27. 16*b* − 2*a*   28. −30*x* − 25*y*
29. −9*m* − 3*n*   30. −7*c* − 35*d*

Exercise 45 *page 53*   1. 5*x* + 3*y*   2. 6*u* + 2*v*   3. 5*a* + 4*b*   4. 2*c* + 5*d*
5. 4*m* + 6*n*   6. 4*p* + 7*q*   7. 2*x* + 7*y*   8. 6*a* + 4*b*
9. 8*c* + 2*d*   10. 5*m* + *n*   11. 5*a* + 5*b*   12. 6*m* + 2*n*
13. 11*p* + *q*   14. 10*u* − 2*v*   15. 13*b* − 3*c*   16. 11*x* + 3*y*
17. 7*a* + *b*   18. 7*c* − 3*d*   19. 10*y* − 10*z*   20. 2*m* − 2*n*
21. 5*p* − 5*q*   22. 3*x* + 3*y*   23. 2*c* − 12*d*   24. 3*m* − 9*n*

21. $\dfrac{10m}{y}, \dfrac{10m}{x}$ 22. $\dfrac{50a}{v}, \dfrac{50a}{u}$ 23. $\dfrac{25t}{q}, \dfrac{25t}{p}$

24. $\dfrac{3V}{h}, \dfrac{3V}{A}$ 25. $\dfrac{RT}{V}, \dfrac{RT}{P}$ 26. $\dfrac{5a}{qr}, \dfrac{5a}{pr}, \dfrac{5a}{pq}$

27. $\dfrac{20t}{yz}, \dfrac{20t}{xz}, \dfrac{20t}{xy}$ 28. $\dfrac{2V}{hl}, \dfrac{2V}{bl}, \dfrac{2V}{bh}$ 29. $\dfrac{3V}{bh}, \dfrac{3V}{ah}, \dfrac{3V}{ab}$

30. $\dfrac{100I}{Rt}, \dfrac{100I}{Pt}, \dfrac{100I}{PR}$

Exercise 56 *page 60*   1. $u - n$ 2. $z - q$ 3. $t - b$ 4. $360° - x$ 5. $p - c$
6. $n - v$ 7. $90° - r$ 8. $t + r$ 9. $v + c$ 10. $m + z$
11. $x + b$ 12. $n + q$ 13. $z + e$ 14. $A - bt$ 15. $P - qz$
16. $V - ct$ 17. $P - at$ 18. $H - kd$ 19. $y - mx$ 20. $E - rI$
21. $180° - 2y$ 22. $M + nt$ 23. $U + vh$ 24. $H + vt$ 25. $S + mt$

Exercise 57 *page 61*   1. $\dfrac{p - q}{n}$ 2. $\dfrac{a - b}{y}$ 3. $\dfrac{E - V}{I}$ 4. $\dfrac{y - c}{x}$

5. $\dfrac{z - k}{t}$ 6. $\dfrac{m + n}{b}$ 7. $\dfrac{r + s}{q}$ 8. $\dfrac{c - d}{2}$

9. $\dfrac{x - y}{5}$ 10. $\dfrac{p - b}{2}$ 11. $\dfrac{360° - n}{3}$ 12. $\dfrac{u + v}{4}$

13. $\dfrac{a + b}{10}$ 14. $\dfrac{x - 3b}{2}, \dfrac{x - 2a}{3}$ 15. $\dfrac{y - 8n}{3}, \dfrac{y - 3m}{8}$ 16. $\dfrac{s - 41}{8}, \dfrac{s - 8w}{4}$

17. $\dfrac{900° - 2y}{5}, \dfrac{900° - 5x}{2}$ 18. $\dfrac{p - \pi d}{2}, \dfrac{p - 21}{\pi}$

19. $\dfrac{t + 5c}{4}$ 20. $\dfrac{z + 7q}{6}$ 21. $\dfrac{a - mn}{3}, \dfrac{a - 3b}{n}, \dfrac{a - 3b}{m}$

22. $\dfrac{p - uv}{5}, \dfrac{p - 5q}{v}, \dfrac{p - 5q}{u}$ 23. $\dfrac{u + xy}{6}$

24. $\dfrac{m + 4n}{q}, \dfrac{m + 4n}{p}$ 25. $\dfrac{c + 9d}{s}, \dfrac{c + 9d}{r}$

26. (a) $\dfrac{v - u}{t}, 10$ (b) $\dfrac{v - u}{a}, 4$

27. (a) $\dfrac{E - V}{I}, 3$ (b) $\dfrac{E - V}{r}, 2$

28. (a) $\dfrac{c + d}{b}, 7$ (b) $\dfrac{c + d}{a}, 12$

29. (a) $\dfrac{p + q}{n}, 5$ (b) $\dfrac{p + q}{m}, 4$

30. $\dfrac{P - p}{t}, \tfrac{1}{4}$

BOOK 4   PART 6

Exercise 59 *page 63*   9. $60°$ 10. $45°$

Exercise 60 *page 64*   1. (a) 4   (b) 3   (c) 2   (d) 5
2. (a) 4   (b) 3   (c) 1   (d) 6
3. (a) 3   (b) 3   (c) 2   (d) 4

4.	(a) 3	(b) 4	(c) 1	(d) 6
5.	(a) 6	(b) 5	(c) 4	(d) 7
6.	(a) 6	(b) 5	(c) 3	(d) 8
7.	(a) 7	(b) 6	(c) 5	(d) 8
8.	(a) 7	(b) 7	(c) 5	(d) 9

9. (a) 2   (b) 2   (c) 1   (d) 2   (e) 2   (f) 1
10. (a) 3   (b) 3   (c) 1   (d) 3   (e) 3   (f) 1

Exercise 61   *page 65*

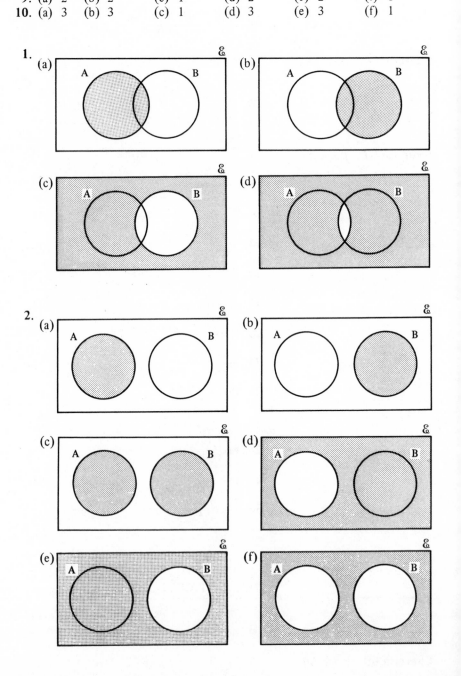

1.
2.

3. (a) A, A∪B   (b) B, A∩B   (c) A′, (A∪B)′   (d) B′, (A∩B)′

Exercise 62 *page 67*   1. $15, 6, 8, 2, 9, 7, 3, 4, 6$ 2. $30, 7, 9, 3, 23, 21, 17, 4, 6$
3. $20, 7, 6, 4, 13, 14, 11, 3, 2$ 4. $25, 18, 15, 12, 7, 10, 4, 6, 3$
5. $7, 3, 2, 12$ 6. $36, 13, 4, 5$
7. $30, 28, 20, 2$ 8. $35, 8, 75$
9. $17, 8, 25$ 10. $72, 18$

Exercise 63 *page 69*   1. $\begin{pmatrix} 3 \\ 5 \end{pmatrix}$ 2. $\begin{pmatrix} 3 \\ 2 \end{pmatrix}$ 3. $\begin{pmatrix} 3 \\ 1 \end{pmatrix}$ 4. $\begin{pmatrix} 3 \\ 0 \end{pmatrix}$ 5. $\begin{pmatrix} 2 \\ 4 \end{pmatrix}$ 6. $\begin{pmatrix} 2 \\ 2 \end{pmatrix}$

7. $\begin{pmatrix} 2 \\ 3 \end{pmatrix}$ 8. $\begin{pmatrix} 1 \\ 5 \end{pmatrix}$ 9. $\begin{pmatrix} 1 \\ 3 \end{pmatrix}$ 10. $\begin{pmatrix} 4 \\ 2 \end{pmatrix}$ 11. $\begin{pmatrix} 4 \\ 3 \end{pmatrix}$ 12. $\begin{pmatrix} 0 \\ 5 \end{pmatrix}$

Exercise 64 *page 71*   1. $\begin{pmatrix} -3 \\ 4 \end{pmatrix}$ 2. $\begin{pmatrix} -3 \\ 1 \end{pmatrix}$ 3. $\begin{pmatrix} -2 \\ 3 \end{pmatrix}$ 4. $\begin{pmatrix} -2 \\ 5 \end{pmatrix}$ 5. $\begin{pmatrix} 3 \\ -5 \end{pmatrix}$ 6. $\begin{pmatrix} 3 \\ -3 \end{pmatrix}$

7. $\begin{pmatrix} 4 \\ -2 \end{pmatrix}$ 8. $\begin{pmatrix} 4 \\ -1 \end{pmatrix}$ 9. $\begin{pmatrix} -2 \\ -4 \end{pmatrix}$ 10. $\begin{pmatrix} -2 \\ -1 \end{pmatrix}$ 11. $\begin{pmatrix} -4 \\ -3 \end{pmatrix}$ 12. $\begin{pmatrix} -4 \\ -1 \end{pmatrix}$

Exercise 65 *page 74*   1. $\begin{pmatrix} 5 \\ 6 \end{pmatrix}$ 2. $\begin{pmatrix} 6 \\ 4 \end{pmatrix}$ 3. $\begin{pmatrix} 8 \\ 5 \end{pmatrix}$ 4. $\begin{pmatrix} 7 \\ 1 \end{pmatrix}$ 5. $\begin{pmatrix} 6 \\ 2 \end{pmatrix}$ 6. $\begin{pmatrix} 9 \\ 1 \end{pmatrix}$

7. $\begin{pmatrix} 5 \\ -2 \end{pmatrix}$ 8. $\begin{pmatrix} 4 \\ -3 \end{pmatrix}$ 9. $\begin{pmatrix} 2 \\ 3 \end{pmatrix}$ 10. $\begin{pmatrix} 1 \\ 6 \end{pmatrix}$ 11. $\begin{pmatrix} -2 \\ 5 \end{pmatrix}$ 12. $\begin{pmatrix} -4 \\ 6 \end{pmatrix}$

13. $\begin{pmatrix} 2 \\ 3 \end{pmatrix}$ 14. $\begin{pmatrix} 3 \\ 1 \end{pmatrix}$ 15. $\begin{pmatrix} -3 \\ -2 \end{pmatrix}$ 16. $\begin{pmatrix} -1 \\ -4 \end{pmatrix}$ 17. $\begin{pmatrix} 2 \\ -3 \end{pmatrix}$ 18. $\begin{pmatrix} 3 \\ -2 \end{pmatrix}$

19. $\begin{pmatrix} -4 \\ 1 \end{pmatrix}$ 20. $\begin{pmatrix} -1 \\ 2 \end{pmatrix}$

Exercise 66 *page 75*   1. $\begin{pmatrix} 100 \\ 150 \end{pmatrix}$ 2. $\begin{pmatrix} 50 \\ 100 \end{pmatrix}$ 3. $\begin{pmatrix} 50 \\ -250 \end{pmatrix}$ 4. $\begin{pmatrix} 150 \\ -100 \end{pmatrix}$ 5. $\begin{pmatrix} 150 \\ -50 \end{pmatrix}$

6. $\begin{pmatrix} -100 \\ 150 \end{pmatrix}$ 7. $\begin{pmatrix} -200 \\ 100 \end{pmatrix}$ 8. $\begin{pmatrix} -100 \\ 150 \end{pmatrix}$ 9. $\begin{pmatrix} -150 \\ -100 \end{pmatrix}$ 10. $\begin{pmatrix} -100 \\ -350 \end{pmatrix}$

11. $\begin{pmatrix} 100 \\ 350 \end{pmatrix}$ 12. $\begin{pmatrix} 300 \\ 50 \end{pmatrix}$ 13. $\begin{pmatrix} 300 \\ 50 \end{pmatrix}$ 14. $\begin{pmatrix} 250 \\ -50 \end{pmatrix}$ 15. $\begin{pmatrix} 100 \\ -150 \end{pmatrix}$

16. $\begin{pmatrix} 200 \\ -100 \end{pmatrix}$ 17. $\begin{pmatrix} -100 \\ 150 \end{pmatrix}$ 18. $\begin{pmatrix} -50 \\ 250 \end{pmatrix}$ 19. $\begin{pmatrix} 50 \\ -250 \end{pmatrix}$ 20. $\begin{pmatrix} -250 \\ 50 \end{pmatrix}$

Exercise 67 *page 76*   1. $\begin{pmatrix} 7 \\ 4 \end{pmatrix}, \begin{pmatrix} 2 \\ 1 \end{pmatrix}, \begin{pmatrix} 2 \\ 1 \end{pmatrix}, \begin{pmatrix} 12 \\ 8 \end{pmatrix}$ 2. $\begin{pmatrix} 6 \\ 5 \end{pmatrix}, \begin{pmatrix} 3 \\ 1 \end{pmatrix}, \begin{pmatrix} 2 \\ 1 \end{pmatrix}, \begin{pmatrix} 3 \\ 9 \end{pmatrix}$

3. $\begin{pmatrix} 6 \\ -3 \end{pmatrix}, \begin{pmatrix} 1 \\ -1 \end{pmatrix}, \begin{pmatrix} 11 \\ -2 \end{pmatrix}, \begin{pmatrix} 4 \\ -10 \end{pmatrix}$ 4. $\begin{pmatrix} 6 \\ -2 \end{pmatrix}, \begin{pmatrix} 4 \\ -3 \end{pmatrix}, \begin{pmatrix} 12 \\ -1 \end{pmatrix}, \begin{pmatrix} 20 \\ -30 \end{pmatrix}$

5. $\begin{pmatrix} -2 \\ 6 \end{pmatrix}, \begin{pmatrix} -2 \\ 3 \end{pmatrix}, \begin{pmatrix} -3 \\ 1 \end{pmatrix}, \begin{pmatrix} -1 \\ 24 \end{pmatrix}$ 6. $\begin{pmatrix} -4 \\ 7 \end{pmatrix}, \begin{pmatrix} -2 \\ 3 \end{pmatrix}, \begin{pmatrix} -4 \\ -1 \end{pmatrix}, \begin{pmatrix} -10 \\ 9 \end{pmatrix}$

7. $\begin{pmatrix} -2 \\ -2 \end{pmatrix}, \begin{pmatrix} -1 \\ -3 \end{pmatrix}, \begin{pmatrix} -3 \\ -2 \end{pmatrix}, \begin{pmatrix} -10 \\ -13 \end{pmatrix}$ 8. $\begin{pmatrix} -3 \\ -3 \end{pmatrix}, \begin{pmatrix} -8 \\ -4 \end{pmatrix}, \begin{pmatrix} 1 \\ 1 \end{pmatrix}, \begin{pmatrix} 2 \\ 0 \end{pmatrix}$

Exercise 68 *page 77*   1. $\frac{1}{5}, \frac{1}{5}, \frac{3}{5}, \frac{2}{5}, \frac{2}{5}$ 2. $\frac{1}{5}, \frac{1}{5}, \frac{2}{5}, \frac{3}{5}$ 3. $\frac{1}{5}, \frac{1}{5}, \frac{2}{5}, \frac{3}{5}$
4. $\frac{2}{7}, \frac{3}{7}, \frac{2}{7}, \frac{5}{7}$ 5. $\frac{2}{7}, \frac{2}{7}, \frac{3}{7}, \frac{2}{7}$

Exercise 69 *page 78*   1. $\frac{3}{7}, \frac{2}{7}$ 2. $\frac{1}{2}, \frac{1}{3}$ 3. $\frac{1}{3}, \frac{1}{3}, \frac{1}{2}, \frac{1}{2}$
4. $\frac{3}{8}, \frac{1}{4}, \frac{1}{2}, \frac{1}{2}$ 5. $\frac{3}{8}, \frac{1}{4}, \frac{5}{8}$ 6. $\frac{3}{10}, \frac{2}{5}, \frac{3}{5}$

7. $\frac{3}{4}, \frac{1}{4}$ 8. $\frac{3}{5}, \frac{2}{5}$ 9. $\frac{5}{6}, \frac{1}{6}$

10. $\frac{1}{2}, \frac{3}{10}, \frac{1}{5}$ 11. $\frac{3}{5}, \frac{1}{3}, \frac{1}{15}$ 12. $\frac{1}{4}, \frac{1}{6}, \frac{1}{4}, \frac{1}{3}, \frac{5}{12}, \frac{7}{12}$

13. $\frac{2}{5}, \frac{1}{4}, \frac{3}{20}, \frac{1}{5}, \frac{3}{5}$ 14. $\frac{1}{6}, \frac{1}{2}, \frac{1}{2}, \frac{1}{3}, \frac{1}{2}, \frac{1}{3}, \frac{1}{2}$ 15. $\frac{5}{12}, \frac{1}{4}, \frac{1}{3}, \frac{1}{3}, \frac{1}{6}$

16. $\frac{1}{4}, \frac{3}{4}, \frac{1}{3}, \frac{1}{2}$ 17. $\frac{1}{4}, \frac{1}{6}, \frac{1}{6}, \frac{1}{3}, \frac{1}{3}, \frac{1}{3}, \frac{7}{12}$ 18. $\frac{3}{8}, \frac{5}{8}, \frac{1}{4}, \frac{3}{8}, \frac{1}{4}, \frac{1}{4}$

19. $\frac{1}{5}, \frac{3}{10}, \frac{1}{10}, \frac{2}{5}, \frac{1}{2}, \frac{3}{10}, \frac{3}{5}$ 20. $\frac{1}{13}, \frac{3}{13}, \frac{9}{13}, \frac{5}{13}, \frac{4}{13}$

Exercise 70 *page 79* 1. $\frac{7}{10}$ 2. $\frac{11}{20}$ 3. $\frac{7}{12}$ 4. $\frac{5}{6}$ 5. $\frac{1}{10}$ 6. $\frac{1}{5}$

7. $\frac{1}{8}$, (5 by 50p, 15 by 10p, 20 by 5p)

8. $\frac{1}{10}$, (2 by £10, 3 by £5, 15 by £1) 9. $\frac{1}{4}$ 10. $\frac{1}{6}$

Revision exercise E
page 80

1. $60°$ 2. $72°$ 3. $8, 4, 3, 2$

4. $57, 88, 25, 180$ 5. $4500, 1500, 42\,000$ 6. $132, 18$

7. $\frac{1}{2}, \frac{1}{3}, \frac{1}{6}$ 8. $\frac{1}{2}, \frac{1}{2}, 1$ 9. $\frac{1}{5}, \frac{4}{5}, \frac{2}{5}, \frac{1}{2}, \frac{3}{5}$

10. $\begin{pmatrix} 150 \\ 50 \end{pmatrix}$ 11. $\begin{pmatrix} 150 \\ 250 \end{pmatrix}$ 12. $\begin{pmatrix} 150 \\ 350 \end{pmatrix}$ 13. $\begin{pmatrix} 300 \\ 100 \end{pmatrix}$ 14. $\begin{pmatrix} 300 \\ 200 \end{pmatrix}$

15. $\begin{pmatrix} 0 \\ 150 \end{pmatrix}$ 16. $\begin{pmatrix} 50 \\ -50 \end{pmatrix}$ 17. $\begin{pmatrix} 50 \\ -200 \end{pmatrix}$ 18. $\begin{pmatrix} 150 \\ -150 \end{pmatrix}$ 19. $\begin{pmatrix} 150 \\ -250 \end{pmatrix}$

20. $\begin{pmatrix} 0 \\ -100 \end{pmatrix}$ 21. $\begin{pmatrix} 0 \\ -300 \end{pmatrix}$ 22. $\begin{pmatrix} -100 \\ 50 \end{pmatrix}$ 23. $\begin{pmatrix} -100 \\ 200 \end{pmatrix}$ 24. $\begin{pmatrix} -150 \\ 150 \end{pmatrix}$

25. $\begin{pmatrix} -300 \\ 50 \end{pmatrix}$ 26. $\begin{pmatrix} 0 \\ 100 \end{pmatrix}$ 27. $\begin{pmatrix} -50 \\ -50 \end{pmatrix}$ 28. $\begin{pmatrix} -50 \\ -250 \end{pmatrix}$ 29. $\begin{pmatrix} -200 \\ -150 \end{pmatrix}$

30. $\begin{pmatrix} -200 \\ -300 \end{pmatrix}$

answers

BOOK 5   PART 1

Exercise 1 *page 1*	**1.** 53	**2.** 42	**3.** 44	**4.** 24	**5.** 26	**6.** 35	**7.** 59	**8.** 25

Exercise 1   *page 1*
1. 53 **2.** 42 **3.** 44 **4.** 24 **5.** 26 **6.** 35 **7.** 59 **8.** 25
9. 36 **10.** 4 **11.** 3 **12.** 3 **13.** 6 **14.** 4 **15.** 5 **16.** 25
17. 21 **18.** 23 **19.** 24 **20.** 16 **21.** 45 **22.** 5 **23.** 9 **24.** 8
25. 41 **26.** 34 **27.** 46 **28.** 26 **29.** 8 **30.** 32

Exercise 2   *page 1*
1. 44 **2.** 17 **3.** 37 **4.** 3 **5.** 12 **6.** 14 **7.** 11 **8.** 16
9. 18 **10.** 41 **11.** 18 **12.** 49 **13.** 13 **14.** 36 **15.** 27 **16.** 12
17. 28 **18.** 16 **19.** 26 **20.** 48 **21.** 38 **22.** 6 **23.** 11 **24.** 15
25. 26 **26.** 28 **27.** 31 **28.** 23 **29.** 18 **30.** 7

Exercise 3   *page 2*
1. (c) **2.** (a) **3.** (b) **4.** (a) **5.** (b) **6.** (c) **7.** (a) **8.** (a)
9. (b) **10.** (c) **11.** (a) **12.** (b) **13.** (b) **14.** (a) **15.** (a) **16.** (c)
17. (a) **18.** (b) **19.** (a) **20.** (b)

Exercise 4   *page 2*
1. (a) **2.** (c) **3.** (a) **4.** (b) **5.** (b) **6.** (b) **7.** (a) **8.** (c)
9. (a) **10.** (a) **11.** (c) **12.** (b) **13.** (b) **14.** (c) **15.** (a) **16.** (b)
17. (a) **18.** (c) **19.** (b) **20.** (a)

Exercise 5   *page 3*
1. 76 **2.** 60 **3.** 23 **4.** 18 **5.** 54 **6.** 36 **7.** 4 **8.** 25
9. 32 **10.** 15 **11.** 65 **12.** 12 **13.** 16 **14.** 5 **15.** 4 **16.** 84
17. 80 **18.** 120 **19.** 120 **20.** 24 **21.** 15 **22.** 42 **23.** 10 **24.** 54
25. 24 **26.** 45 **27.** 2 **28.** 3 **29.** 4 **30.** 2

Exercise 6   *page 4*
1. 30 **2.** 50 **3.** 50 **4.** 80 **5.** 20 **6.** 90 **7.** 90 **8.** 20
9. 10 **10.** 70 **11.** 40 **12.** 100 **13.** 170 **14.** 150 **15.** 150 **16.** 320
17. 540 **18.** 280 **19.** 110 **20.** 610 **21.** 470 **22.** 100 **23.** 200 **24.** 190
25. 310 **26.** (a) 200 (b) 400 (c) 500
27. (a) 300 (b) 600 (c) 700 **28.** (a) 100 (b) 300 (c) 500
29. (a) 300 (b) 400 (c) 700 **30.** (a) 200 (b) 100 (c) 500
31. (a) 700 (b) 900 (c) 500 **32.** (a) 600 (b) 700 (c) 1000
33. (a) 900 (b) 800 (c) 500 **34.** (a) 900 (b) 800 (c) 600
35. (a) 100 (b) 200 (c) 300 **36.** 1640 **37.** 3480 **38.** 7280
39. 2850 **40.** 4560 **41.** 6730 **42.** 1600 **43.** 5100
44. 1900 **45.** 7400 **46.** 5400 **47.** 2700 **48.** 6200
49. 3300 **50.** 3000 **51.** 2000 **52.** 3000 **53.** 3000
54. 6000 **55.** 5000 **56.** 9000 **57.** 6000
58. (a) 1690 (b) 1700 (c) 2000 **59.** (a) 3480 (b) 3500 (c) 3000
60. (a) 2140 (b) 2100 (c) 2000 **61.** (a) 4310 (b) 4300 (c) 4000

62. (a) 3720 (b) 3700 (c) 4000   **63.** (a) 5860 (b) 5900 (c) 6000
64. (a) 2570 (b) 2600 (c) 3000   **65.** (a) 1360 (b) 1400 (c) 1000
66. (a) 7430 (b) 7400 (c) 7000   **67.** (a) 2610 (b) 2600 (c) 3000
68. (a) 3800 (b) 3800 (c) 4000   **69.** (a) 4080 (b) 4100 (c) 4000
70. (a) 8030 (b) 8000 (c) 8000

Exercise 7   *page 4*

1. £17·90, £18, £20   **2.** £36·90, £37, £40   **3.** £57·10, £57, £60
4. £42·40, £42, £40   **5.** £63·30, £63, £60   **6.** £24·80, £25, £20
7. £38·20, £38, £40   **8.** £14·50, £15, £10   **9.** £53·00, £53, £50
10. £49·80, £50, £50   **11.** £26·10, £26, £30   **12.** £30·80, £31, £30

Exercise 8   *page 5*

1. 1·4   **2.** 4·6   **3.** 5·6   **4.** 3·4   **5.** 6·3   **6.** 8·8
7. 7·9   **8.** 8·1   **9.** 0·9   **10.** 5·1   **11.** 2·0   **12.** 5·0
13. 3·0   **14.** 1·54   **15.** 3·95   **16.** 2·62   **17.** 6·58   **18.** 4·29
19. 0·89   **20.** 5·97   **21.** 1·66   **22.** 6·12   **23.** 4·51   **24.** 3·40
25. 2·01   **26.** 1·40   **27.** 5·70   **28.** 5·00   **29.** 2·00   **30.** 3·99
31. 1·3   **32.** 2·5   **33.** 5·4   **34.** 4·7   **35.** 3·9   **36.** 2·1
37. 0·9   **38.** 1·4   **39.** 5·0   **40.** 5·0   **41.** (a) 4·37 (b) 4·4
42. (a) 2·54 (b) 2·5   **43.** (a) 1·72 (b) 1·7   **44.** (a) 0·58 (b) 0·6
45. (a) 5·25 (b) 5·3   **46.** (a) 6·87 (b) 6·9   **47.** (a) 1·40 (b) 1·4
48. (a) 4·98 (b) 5·0   **49.** (a) 3·00 (b) 3·0   **50.** (a) 3·02 (b) 3·0
51. (a) 4·04 (b) 4·0   **52.** (a) 5·07 (b) 5·1   **53.** (a) 1·09 (b) 1·1
54. (a) 2·41 (b) 2·4   **55.** (a) 3·20 (b) 3·2   **56.** (a) 4·01 (b) 4·0
57. (a) 5·00 (b) 5·0   **58.** (a) 6·10 (b) 6·1   **59.** (a) 1·06 (b) 1·1
60. (a) 0·56 (b) 0·6

Exercise 9   *page 5*

1. 50   **2.** 70   **3.** 280   **4.** 800   **5.** 34·3
6. 25·9   **7.** 54·81   **8.** 25·07   **9.** 62   **10.** 54
11. 6   **12.** 400   **13.** 900   **14.** 1800   **15.** 9000
16. 723·8   **17.** 500·1   **18.** 245   **19.** 813   **20.** 76
21. 530   **22.** 720   **23.** 3000   **24.** 8000   **25.** 52 000
26. 70 000   **27.** 5431   **28.** 7005   **29.** 842   **30.** 4350
31. 6270   **32.** 6700   **33.** 400   **34.** 32·4   **35.** 91·7
36. 57   **37.** 4·8   **38.** 3·7   **39.** 6   **40.** 45·36
41. 53·07   **42.** 3·627   **43.** 8·005   **44.** 0·481   **45.** 0·28
46. 0·043   **47.** 25·48   **48.** 78·2   **49.** 84   **50.** 6·31
51. 3·02   **52.** 8·5   **53.** 7   **54.** 0·57   **55.** 0·25
56. 7·395   **57.** 4·032   **58.** 0·5607   **59.** 0·306   **60.** 0·0534
61. 0·0829   **62.** 3·724   **63.** 4·21   **64.** 2·5   **65.** 0·853
66. 0·27   **67.** 0·4   **68.** 0·035   **69.** 0·052   **70.** 0·04

Exercise 10   *page 6*

1. $1·754 \times 10^3$ **2.** $2·139 \times 10^3$ **3.** $5·627 \times 10^3$
4. $4·071 \times 10^3$ **5.** $3·48 \times 10^3$ **6.** $1·92 \times 10^3$
7. $2·5 \times 10^3$ **8.** $3·9 \times 10^3$ **9.** $5·0 \times 10^3$
10. $8·0 \times 10^3$ **11.** $3·72 \times 10^2$ **12.** $9·16 \times 10^2$
13. $4·95 \times 10^2$ **14.** $1·09 \times 10^2$ **15.** $2·6 \times 10^2$
16. $5·8 \times 10^2$ **17.** $6·0 \times 10^2$ **18.** $9·0 \times 10^2$
19. $2·714 \times 10^2$ **20.** $5·327 \times 10^2$ **21.** $8·045 \times 10^2$
22. $3·009 \times 10^2$ **23.** $4·5 \times 10^1$ **24.** $9·1 \times 10^1$
25. $7·0 \times 10^1$ **26.** $4·0 \times 10^1$ **27.** $3·73 \times 10^1$
28. $7·06 \times 10^1$ **29.** $2·452 \times 10^1$ **30.** $5·039 \times 10^1$

Exercise 11   *page 6*

1. 53·72	**2.** 25·61	**3.** 13·9	**4.** 45	**5.** 416·5
6. 356	**7.** 630	**8.** 2425	**9.** 8540	**10.** 7800
11. 10^1	**12.** 10^1	**13.** 10^1	**14.** 10^2	**15.** 10^2
16. 10^2	**17.** 10^2	**18.** 10^3	**19.** 10^3	**20.** 10^3
21. 3·512	**22.** 5·34	**23.** 6·5	**24.** 4·326	**25.** 5·37
26. 8·4	**27.** 2·415	**28.** 3·57	**29.** 6·4	**30.** 7

Exercise 12   *page 7*

1. 1936	**2.** 4572	**3.** 8126	**4.** 5093	**5.** 2730
6. 9150	**7.** 6800	**8.** 7400	**9.** 2000	**10.** 7000
11. 932	**12.** 156	**13.** 819	**14.** 405	**15.** 630
16. 490	**17.** 300	**18.** 500	**19.** 531·6	**20.** 495·1
21. 107·5	**22.** 610·4	**23.** 67	**24.** 84	**25.** 80
26. 60	**27.** 55·3	**28.** 10·5	**29.** 94·36	**30.** 80·05

Exercise 13   *page 7*

1. $8·0 \times 10^3$	**2.** $9·0 \times 10^3$	**3.** $4·0 \times 10^3$	**4.** $6·0 \times 10^3$
5. $5·0 \times 10^3$	**6.** $6·0 \times 10^3$	**7.** $7·0 \times 10^3$	**8.** $5·0 \times 10^2$
9. $9·0 \times 10^2$	**10.** $9·0 \times 10^2$	**11.** $1·4 \times 10^3$	**12.** $1·5 \times 10^3$
13. $2·4 \times 10^3$	**14.** $2·0 \times 10^3$	**15.** $3·0 \times 10^3$	**16.** $2·4 \times 10^4$
17. $3·6 \times 10^4$	**18.** $4·9 \times 10^4$	**19.** $4·8 \times 10^4$	**20.** $4·0 \times 10^4$

Exercise 14   *page 8*

1. $\frac{31}{100}$	**2.** $\frac{7}{10}$	**3.** $\frac{1}{10}$	**4.** $\frac{2}{5}$	**5.** $\frac{3}{5}$	**6.** $\frac{1}{2}$
7. $\frac{3}{4}$	**8.** $\frac{9}{20}$	**9.** $\frac{11}{20}$	**10.** $\frac{1}{20}$	**11.** 29%	**12.** 81%
13. 7%	**14.** 30%	**15.** 90%	**16.** 15%	**17.** 35%	**18.** 80%
19. 20%	**20.** 25%	**21.** (c)	**22.** (a)	**23.** (b)	**24.** (a)
25. (b)	**26.** (b)	**27.** (c)	**28.** (a)	**29.** (b)	**30.** (c)

Exercise 15   *page 8*

1. £45	**2.** £19	**3.** £60	**4.** £72	**5.** £51
6. £162	**7.** £133	**8.** £375	**9.** £108	**10.** £136
11. £40·50	**12.** £25·60	**13.** £31·50	**14.** £47·50	**15.** £25·50
16. £112·50	**17.** £86·40	**18.** £82·50	**19.** £199·50	**20.** £127·50

Exercise 16   *page 9*

1. £30, £230	**2.** £75, £575	**3.** £900, £6900
4. £180, £1380	**5.** £12, £92	**6.** £21, £161
7. £27, £207	**8.** £7·50, £57·50	**9.** £13·50, £103·50
10. £16·50, £126·50	**11.** £31·50, £241·50	**12.** £2·40, £18·40
13. £4·20, £32·20	**14.** £1·35, £10·35	**15.** 72p, £5·52
16. 81p, £6·21	**17.** £1·23, £9·43	**18.** £1·89, £14·49
19. £1·98, £15·18	**20.** £2·34, £17·94	

Exercise 17   *page 9*

1. £32	**2.** £54	**3.** £40	**4.** £42	**5.** £35	**6.** £36
7. £90	**8.** £80	**9.** £30	**10.** £75	**11.** £240	**12.** £30
13. £18	**14.** £20	**15.** £18	**16.** £9	**17.** £24	**18.** £6
19. £3	**20.** £6				

Exercise 18   *page 10*

1. £60	**2.** £90	**3.** £48	**4.** £60	**5.** £150	**6.** £90
7. £200	**8.** £160	**9.** £240	**10.** £300	**11.** £400	**12.** £100
13. £45	**14.** £120	**15.** £36	**16.** £30	**17.** £105	**18.** £60
19. £16	**20.** £36	**21.** £1200	**22.** £288	**23.** £60	**24.** £30
25. £4	**26.** £6	**27.** (a) by £20		**28.** (b) by £6	
29. (a) by £3		**30.** (a) by £6			

BOOK 5   PART 2

Exercise 19	*page 11*				
1. 130°	**2.** 145°	**3.** 105°	**4.** 40°	**5.** 55°	**6.** 25°
7. 50°	**8.** 60°	**9.** 60°	**10.** 110°	**11.** 150°	**12.** 90°
13. 60°, 60°		**14.** 100°, 100°		**15.** 40°, 80°	
16. 110°, 40°		**17.** 50°, 90°		**18.** 120°, 30°	
19. 40°, 40°, 100°		**20.** 100°, 40°, 40°			

Exercise 20   *page 12*

1. 45°, 45°, 135°   **2.** 125°, 125°, 55°   **3.** 35°, 35°, 145°
4. 115°, 115°, 65°   **5.** 45°, 85°   **6.** 70°, 110°, 110°
7. 60°   **8.** 50°   **9.** 135°
10. 125°, 105°   **11.** 140°, 40°, 40°   **12.** 115°, 90°
13. 40°, 40°, 20°   **14.** 30°, 30°, 80°   **15.** 25°, 25°, 105°, 50°
16. 95°, 30°, 125°, 25°   **17.** 45°, 135°   **18.** 72°, 108°
19. 100°, 80°, 30°   **20.** 120°, 60°, 90°   **21.** 130°, 50°, 50°, 130°
22. 135°, 135°, 45°   **23.** 60°, 60°, 120°   **24.** 60°, 120°, 60°
25. 140°, 70°, 40°

Exercise 21   *page 14*

1. 1:100   **2.** 1:500   **3.** 1:200   **4.** 1:2000
5. 1:5000   **6.** 1:2500   **7.** 1:10 000   **8.** 1:50
9. 1:20   **10.** 1:25   **11.** 1:100 000   **12.** 1:500 000
13. 1:200 000   **14.** 1:20 000   **15.** 1:25 000

Exercise 22   *page 15*

1. 120 cm by 90 cm   **2.** 80 cm by 200 cm   **3.** 250 cm by 125 cm
4. 18 m   **5.** 15 m by 12 m   **6.** 10 m, 4 m and 2 m
7. 12 m, 9 m and 7·5 m   **8.** 60 m   **9.** 70 m   **10.** 1:2000, 120 m

Exercise 23   *page 16*

1. 20 cm by 10 cm   **2.** 20 cm by 12 cm   **3.** 36 cm
4. 6 cm   **5.** 20 cm by 12 cm   **6.** 8 cm by 5 cm
7. 20 cm by 15 cm by 10 cm   **8.** 24 cm   **9.** 8 cm
10. 1:1200, 7 cm

Exercise 24   *page 16*

1. 040°   **2.** 070°   **3.** 130°   **4.** 150°   **5.** 180°
6. 210°   **7.** 260°   **8.** 240°   **9.** 200°   **10.** 220°
11. 330°   **12.** 290°   **13.** 320°   **14.** 280°   **15.** 340°

Exercise 25   *page 17*

1. 100 km, 270°   **2.** 70 km, 270°   **3.** 80 km, 270°
4. 80 km, 270°   **5.** 40 km, 270°   **6.** 140 km, 90°
7. 50 km, 90°   **8.** 100 km, 90°   **9.** 120 km, 90°
10. 140 km, 90°

Exercise 26   *page 19*

1. AĈB, AD̂B   **2.** XŴY, XẐY
3. PR̂Q, PQ̂R   **4.** UŴV, UV̂W
5. LN̂M, LM̂N, ML̂N   **6.** FĤG, FĜH, GF̂H
7. AB̂C, CD̂E, AĈB, DĈE   **8.** PQ̂R, RŜT, PR̂Q, SR̂T, RT̂S
9. UV̂W, WX̂Y, UŴV, XŴY, VÛW   **10.** LP̂M, MP̂N, LM̂P, NM̂P
11. AB̂C, BÂD, AĈB and AD̂B   **12.** QP̂S, PQ̂R, PR̂Q and PŜQ

Exercise 27   *page 20*

1. 60° 30°   **2.** 70° 35°   **3.** 90° 45°   **4.** 50° 25°   **5.** 120° 60°
6. 140° 70°   **7.** 150° 75°

Exercise 28 *page 22*   **1.** 20°   **2.** 36°   **3.** 65°   **4.** 72°   **5.** 54°
6. 90°   **7.** 26°   **8.** 36°   **9.** 64°   **10.** 110°
11. 170°   **12.** 136°

Exercise 29 *page 23*   **1.** 80° 40° 40° 40°   **2.** 100° 50° 50° 50°   **3.** 120° 60° 60° 60°
4. 160° 80° 80° 80°   **5.** 90° 45° 45° 45°

Exercise 30 *page 24*   **1.** 40°   **2.** 25°   **3.** 50°, 30°   **4.** 35°, 40°   **5.** 60°, 25°
6. 30°, 35°   **7.** 45°, 60°   **8.** 50°, 40°

Exercise 31 *page 24*   **1. to 5.** 90°

Exercise 32 *page 25*   **1.** 20°   **2.** 40°   **3.** 60°   **4.** 15°   **5.** 65°
6. 45°   **7.** 70°   **8.** 35°   **9.** 25°   **10.** 50°, 40°, 40°

BOOK 5   PART 3

Exercise 34 *page 32*   **1.** (a) £1·20   (b) £2   (c) 20p   (d) 6 kg   (e) $2\frac{1}{2}$ kg   (f) $4\frac{1}{2}$ kg
2. (a) 80p   (b) £1·80   (c) £3·40   (d) £2·30   (e) 3 litres
(f) 7 litres   (g) 13 litres   (h) 15·5 litres
3. (a) £9   (b) £15   (c) £13·50   (d) 10 litres   (e) 25 litres
(f) 15 litres
4. (a) £6   (b) £15   (c) £27   (d) 6 m²   (e) 20 m²   (f) 14 m²
5. (a) £90   (b) £150   (c) £105   (d) 5 m²   (e) 22·5 m²   (f) 7·5 m²
6. (a) 90p   (b) 75p   (c) £1·05   (d) 15 min   (e) 8 min   (f) 28 min
7. (a) £1·80   (b) £1·08   (c) 36   (d) 6
8. (a) 240 km   (b) 200 km   (c) 280 km   (d) 4 h   (e) $1\frac{1}{2}$ h   (f) $\frac{1}{2}$ h
9. (a) 54 km   (b) 45 km   (c) 42 km   (d) 12 km   (e) $1\frac{1}{2}$ h   (f) $\frac{1}{2}$ h
(g) 1 h 20 min   (h) 1 h 40 min
10. (a) 9 km   (b) $7\frac{1}{2}$ km   (c) 4 km   (d) 45 min   (e) 1 h 20 min
(f) 20 min

Exercise 35 *page 33*   **1.** (a) 24 km   (b) 4 km   (c) 7·5 miles   (d) 12·5 miles
2. (a) 2·5 kg   (b) 4 kg   (c) 9 kg   (d) 16·5 lb   (e) 27·5 lb   (f) 24·2 lb
3. (a) 12 litres   (b) 14 litres   (c) 2 litres   (d) 7 pints
(e) 17·5 pints   (f) 10·5 pints
4. (a) 48 litres   (b) 80 litres   (c) 3·5 gallons
5. (a) S27   (b) S4·50   (c) £6   (d) £10
6. (a) Fr27   (b) Fr36   (c) Fr63   (d) £6   (e) £8   (f) £9
7. (a) DM57   (b) DM47·50   (c) £5   (d) £7·50
8. (a) 60 g   (b) 48 g   (c) 32 g   (d) 11 cm³   (e) 8 cm³   (f) 2·5 cm³
9. (a) 12 kg   (b) 18 kg   (c) 6 kg   (d) 10 kg   (e) 5 litres
(f) 17·5 litres   (g) 8 litres   (h) 14 litres
10. (a) 210 g   (b) 245 g   (c) 35 g   (d) 1 m   (e) 1·5 m   (f) 2·5 m

Exercise 36 *page 35*   **1.** (a) Reading, Didcot, Bristol Parkway, Newport
(b) 09.15, 10.00, 11.00

2. (a) Dishforth, Leeming Bar, Durham
   (b) 10.30, 11.30, 11.45
3. (a) Sherbrook Valley Head, The Stepping Stones, Shugborough Hall
   (b) 15.00, 15.30, 15.45
4. (a) Great Sankey, Rainhill, Liverpool
   (b) 14.30, 15.15
5. (a) Stannington, Morpeth, Alnwick, Warrenford, Berwick-on-Tweed
   (b) 11.15, 11.30, 12.30, 12.45
6. (a) Dorrington, Church Stretton, Craven Arms
   (b) 16.45, 18.30, 18.45
7. (a) Halesowen, Tenbury Wells, New Radnor, Llangurig, Aberystwyth
   (b) 08.30, 08.45, 09.15, 10.15
8. (a) Hinckley, Leicester, Thorney, Wisbech
   (b) 09.30, 10.00, 10.30, 10.45, 12.00

Exercise 37   *page 38*

1. 10.00, 10.30, 60 km, 2 h, 70 km/h
2. 13.00, 14.30, 1 h, 3 km/h
3. 09.00, 11.30, 120 km, 60 km/h
4. 11.00, 11.30, 4 h, 64 km/h
5. 08.30, 09.30, 4 h 30 min, 88 km/h
6. 50 km/h, 60 km, 16.30, 17.00, 45 km/h
7. 120 km/h, 3 h 30 min, 70 km, 14.30, 15.00, 100 km/h

Revision exercise A
page 41

5. 135
6. (a) Woking, Andover, Salisbury, Yeovil
   (b) 06.15, 07.00, 07.15, 09.15, 09.45
7. (a) Hemel Hempstead, Tamworth, Crewe, Lancaster, Carlisle
   (b) 14.30, 15.30, 16.00, 16.45
8. 45 km/h, 4 h, 60 km, 16.30, 17.30, 60 km/h
9. 40 km/h, 3 h, 15 km, 16.00, 16.30, 30 km/h
10. 80 km/h, 3 h 30 min, 30 km, 15.30, 16.00, 125 km/h

BOOK 5   PART 4

Exercise 38   *page 45*

1. 88 cm	2. 132 cm	3. 22 cm
4. 176 mm	5. 264 mm	6. 220 mm
7. 660 cm	8. 44 cm	9. 440 cm
10. 880 cm	11. 308 mm	12. 352 mm
13. 6·284 cm	14. 15·71 cm	15. 157·1 cm
16. 31·42 cm	17. 9·426 mm	18. 154 cm^2
19. 1386 cm^2	20. 15 400 cm^2	21. 38·5 mm^2
22. 346·5 mm^2	23. 616 mm^2	24. 9·625 cm^2
25. 314·2 cm^2	26. 12·568 cm^2	27. 3·142 cm^2
28. 78·55 mm^2	29. 28·278 mm^2	30. 1256·8 cm^2

Exercise 39   *page 45*

1. 400 m   2. 200 m   3. 500 cm   4. 400 cm   5. 25 m
6. 200 m   7. 130 cm, 320 mm   8. 150 cm, 110 cm, 56 cm
9. 260 mm

Exercise 40   *page 47*   **1.** 8   **2.** 66 mm^2 **3.** 314 cm^2, 2512 cm^2, 5024 cm^2, 7536 cm^2
4. Both 616 cm^2 **5.** 3850 mm^2 **6.** 3250 cm^2
7. 86 mm^2, 118 cm^2 **8.** 30 cm^2, 90 cm^2 **9.** 98 cm^2, 91 cm^2
10. 297 cm^2

Exercise 41   *page 49*   **1.** $\frac{1}{9}$ **2.** $\frac{1}{10}$ **3.** $\frac{1}{2}$ **4.** $\frac{1}{12}$ **5.** $\frac{1}{15}$ **6.** $\frac{2}{3}$ **7.** $\frac{2}{5}$ **8.** $\frac{2}{9}$
9. $\frac{3}{4}$ **10.** $\frac{3}{10}$ **11.** $\frac{3}{8}$ **12.** $\frac{5}{6}$ **13.** $\frac{5}{8}$ **14.** $\frac{5}{12}$ **15.** $\frac{7}{12}$ **16.** $\frac{7}{10}$

Exercise 42   *page 49*   **1.** 25 cm   **2.** 50 cm   **3.** 30 cm   **4.** 25 mm   **5.** 250 mm
6. 25 mm   **7.** 80 cm   **8.** 20 cm   **9.** 25 mm   **10.** 15 mm
11. 12 mm   **12.** 24 cm   **13.** 20 cm   **14.** 35 mm   **15.** 10 mm
16. 50 cm, 70 cm   **17.** 2 cm, 4 cm, 1 cm, 3 cm
18. 45 cm, 60 cm, 90 cm, 135 cm, 15 cm   **19.** 4 cm, 6 cm, 3 cm or 9 cm

Exercise 43   *page 50*   **1.** 60°   **2.** 30°   **3.** 90°   **4.** 180°   **5.** 120°
6. 45°   **7.** 24°   **8.** 72°   **9.** 300°   **10.** 210°
11. 150°   **12.** 135°   **13.** 225°   **14.** 108°   **15.** 144°

Exercise 44   *page 51*   **1.** 22 cm   **2.** 33 cm   **3.** 44 mm   **4.** 11 cm   **5.** 5·5 cm
6. 22 mm   **7.** 4·71 cm   **8.** 1·57 cm   **9.** 12·56 mm   **10.** 4·71 mm
11. 7·85 cm   **12.** 3·14 cm
13. 264 mm, 132 mm, 44 mm, 66 mm, 88 mm, 176 mm, 198 mm, 220 mm
14. 264 mm, 132 mm, 44 mm, 88 mm, 66 mm, 176 mm, 220 mm, 198 mm

Revision exercise B   **1.** (a) 8 mm   (b) 120°   (c) 40 mm
page 52   **2.** (a) 22 cm   (b) 99 cm   (c) 66 cm   (d) 132 cm   (e) 44 cm
(f) 33 cm
3. (a) 132 cm   (b) 22 cm   (c) 66 cm   (d) 44 cm
4. 110 cm   **5.** 15 m

BOOK 5   PART 5

Exercise 45   *page 53*   **1.** $2x + 2y$ **2.** $4m + 4n$ **3.** $5u + 5v$ **4.** $3a - 3b$ **5.** $6p - 6q$
6. $4y - 4z$ **7.** $3x + 6$ **8.** $4t + 12$ **9.** $5r + 5$ **10.** $2a - 12$
11. $6b - 30$ **12.** $8 + 4m$ **13.** $15 + 5n$ **14.** $24 - 3p$ **15.** $25 - 5q$
16. $ab + ac$ **17.** $xy + xz$ **18.** $pq - pr$ **19.** $bc - bd$ **20.** $m^2 + mn$
21. $u^2 + uv$ **22.** $a^2 - ab$ **23.** $x^2 - xy$ **24.** $pq - p^2$ **25.** $de - d^2$
26. $mn + 3m$ **27.** $pq + 5p$ **28.** $x^2 + 2x$ **29.** $t^2 + 4t$ **30.** $ab - 6a$
31. $uv - u$ **32.** $z^2 - 3z$ **33.** $c^2 - 7c$ **34.** $4p - pq$ **35.** $7r - rs$
36. $8a - a^2$ **37.** $5b - b^2$ **38.** $2xy + 2xz$ **39.** $3pq + 3pr$ **40.** $6de + 6df$
41. $5ab - 5ac$ **42.** $4tu - 4tv$ **43.** $3b^2 + 3bc$ **44.** $6m^2 + 6mn$ **45.** $4r^2 - 4rs$
46. $7x^2 - 7xy$ **47.** $4cd - 4c^2$ **48.** $6yz - 6y^2$ **49.** $3ab + 12a$ **50.** $2xy + 10x$
51. $4p^2 + 8p$

Exercise 46   *page 53*   **1.** $ab + 4a + 3b + 12$ **2.** $mn + 5m + 2n + 10$ **3.** $cd + 6c + 4d + 24$
4. $uv + 3u + v + 3$ **5.** $bc + 2b + 2c + 4$ **6.** $pq + 2p + 4q + 8$
7. $xy + 3x + 6y + 18$ **8.** $ef + 4e + 5f + 20$ **9.** $rs + r + 5s + 5$
10. $yz + y + z + 1$ **11.** $xy - 4x - 2y + 8$ **12.** $pq - 5p - 3q + 15$

13. $uv - 6u - 5v + 30$ 　 14. $ab - 4a - b + 4$ 　 15. $mn - 3m - 3n + 9$
16. $rs - 5r - 5s + 25$ 　 17. $yz - 3y - 4z + 12$ 　 18. $cd - 2c - 6d + 12$
19. $uv - 3u - 5v + 15$ 　 20. $xy - x - 3y + 3$ 　 21. $pq - 5p + 3q - 15$
22. $xy - 6x + 2y - 12$ 　 23. $ab - 7a + 4b - 28$ 　 24. $mn - 2m + n - 2$
25. $yz - 4y + 4z - 16$ 　 26. $rs - 10r + 10s - 100$ 　 27. $bc - 4b + 6c - 24$
28. $mn - 2m + 8n - 16$ 　 29. $xy - 3x + 7y - 21$ 　 30. $ab - a + 6b - 6$
31. $mn + 4m - 2n - 8$ 　 32. $xy + 8x - 3y - 24$ 　 33. $cd + 7c - 2d - 14$
34. $pq + 5p - q - 5$ 　 35. $ab + 6a - 6b - 36$ 　 36. $yz + 9y - 2z - 18$

Exercise 47　*page 54*

1. $x^2 + 7x + 12$ 　 2. $y^2 + 9y + 20$ 　 3. $z^2 + 8z + 12$
4. $t^2 + 14t + 45$ 　 5. $a^2 + 4a + 3$ 　 6. $b^2 + 8b + 7$
7. $p^2 + 8p + 15$ 　 8. $q^2 + 10q + 16$ 　 9. $r^2 + 10r + 24$
10. $s^2 + 15s + 50$ 　 11. $t^2 + 6t + 5$ 　 12. $u^2 + 10u + 9$
13. $a^2 - 7a + 10$ 　 14. $b^2 - 9b + 18$ 　 15. $c^2 - 12c + 32$
16. $d^2 - 17d + 60$ 　 17. $e^2 - 5e + 4$ 　 18. $f^2 - 11f + 10$
19. $x^2 - 6x + 8$ 　 20. $y^2 - 10y + 21$ 　 21. $z^2 - 11z + 30$
22. $t^2 - 14t + 48$ 　 23. $u^2 - 3u + 2$ 　 24. $v^2 - 7v + 6$
25. $a^2 + 2a - 15$ 　 26. $b^2 + 4b - 21$ 　 27. $c^2 + 2c - 8$
28. $d^2 + 3d - 40$ 　 29. $x^2 + x - 6$ 　 30. $y^2 + 4y - 5$
31. $z^2 + z - 2$ 　 32. $m^2 - 4m - 12$ 　 33. $n^2 - 2n - 15$
34. $p^2 - 4p - 32$ 　 35. $q^2 - 2q - 80$ 　 36. $r^2 - r - 12$
37. $s^2 - 2s - 3$ 　 38. $x^2 - 3x - 10$ 　 39. $y^2 - 5y - 24$
40. $z^2 - 7z - 18$ 　 41. $t^2 - 3t - 28$ 　 42. $a^2 - a - 20$

Exercise 48　*page 54*

1. $a^2 + 8a + 16$ 　 2. $b^2 + 12b + 36$ 　 3. $c^2 + 14c + 49$
4. $x^2 + 24x + 144$ 　 5. $y^2 + 40y + 400$ 　 6. $p^2 - 4p + 4$
7. $q^2 - 16q + 64$ 　 8. $r^2 - 20r + 100$ 　 9. $m^2 - 60m + 900$
10. $n^2 - 80n + 1600$ 　 11. $t^2 - 25$ 　 12. $u^2 - 81$
13. $v^2 - 1$ 　 14. $d^2 - 121$ 　 15. $e^2 - 2500$

Exercise 49　*page 55*

1. 3535 　 2. 8787 　 3. 16 564 　 4. 4182 　 5. 1938 　 6. 5610
7. 1339 　 8. 2472 　 9. 7313 　 10. 2475 　 11. 3564 　 12. 5346
13. 3136 　 14. 2352 　 15. 4998 　 16. 7350 　 17. 1455 　 18. 2037
19. 3201 　 20. 5917

Exercise 50　*page 55*

1. 480 　 2. 530 　 3. 720 　 4. 370 　 5. 290 　 6. 5700
7. 9400 　 8. 3900 　 9. 7600 　 10. 4800 　 11. 9200 　 12. 7100
13. 8700 　 14. 4500 　 15. 2700 　 16. 53 000 　 17. 75 000 　 18. 62 000
19. 84 000 　 20. 26 000 　 21. 50 　 22. 80 　 23. 120 　 24. 25
25. 900 　 26. 700 　 27. 40 　 28. 110 　 29. 60 　 30. 15
31. 35 　 32. 300 　 33. 800 　 34. 90 　 35. 120 　 36. 70
37. 45 　 38. 75 　 39. 600 　 40. 1100 　 41. 16 　 42. 25
43. 52 　 44. 210 　 45. 360 　 46. 540 　 47. 243 　 48. 756
49. 31·5 　 50. 64·8 　 51. 126 　 52. 549 　 53. 801 　 54. 54
55. 4500 　 56. 3200 　 57. 700 　 58. 860 　 59. 930 　 60. 80

Exercise 51　*page 56*

1. $4(x + y)$ 　 2. $3(u + v)$ 　 3. $6(a + b)$ 　 4. $9(m + n)$
5. $7(p + q)$ 　 6. $2(a^2 + b^2)$ 　 7. $5(x^2 + y^2)$ 　 8. $8(u^2 + v^2)$
9. $10(m^2 + n^2)$ 　 10. $6(p - q)$ 　 11. $3(a - b)$ 　 12. $9(x - y)$
13. $7(m - n)$ 　 14. $5(u^2 - v^2)$ 　 15. $8(x^2 - y^2)$ 　 16. $9(a^2 - b^2)$
17. $3(p^2 - q^2)$ 　 18. $a(m + n)$ 　 19. $b(u + v)$ 　 20. $c(x + y)$
21. $d(p + q)$ 　 22. $m(u^2 + v^2)$ 　 23. $n(r^2 + s^2)$ 　 24. $p(x^2 + y^2)$
25. $q(a^2 + b^2)$ 　 26. $m(x - y)$ 　 27. $n(u - v)$ 　 28. $p(a - b)$

29. $q(c-d)$ **30.** $a(r^2-s^2)$ **31.** $b(p^2-q^2)$ **32.** $c(x^2-y^2)$
33. $d(m^2-n^2)$ **34.** $x(x+y)$ **35.** $p(p+q)$ **36.** $u(u+v)$
37. $a(a+b)$ **38.** $r(r+s)$ **39.** $c(c-d)$ **40.** $y(y-z)$
41. $m(m-n)$ **42.** $t(t-u)$ **43.** $c(b+c)$ **44.** $e(d+e)$
45. $z(y+z)$ **46.** $p(n+p)$ **47.** $l(k+l)$ **48.** $r(q-r)$
49. $f(e-f)$ **50.** $t(s-t)$ **51.** $m(l-m)$ **52.** $d(c-d)$
53. $x^2(a+b)$ **54.** $y^2(c+d)$ **55.** $t^2(m+n)$ **56.** $z^2(p+q)$
57. $u^2(k-l)$ **58.** $v^2(q-r)$ **59.** $r^2(b-c)$ **60.** $s^2(d-e)$

Exercise 52   *page 57*

1. $2(a+b)$ **2.** $8(c+d)$ **3.** $3(m+n)$ **4.** $9(x-y)$
5. $5(u-v)$ **6.** $12(p-q)$ **7.** $2(a+3b)$ **8.** $2(c+5d)$
9. $3(m+4n)$ **10.** $3(p+7q)$ **11.** $5(u+2v)$ **12.** $5(x+5y)$
13. $3(b-5c)$ **14.** $3(d-8e)$ **15.** $4(r-3s)$ **16.** $4(y-5z)$
17. $6(m-3n)$ **18.** $6(t-5u)$ **19.** $2(4x+y)$ **20.** $2(6u+v)$
21. $3(6p+q)$ **22.** $3(10m+n)$ **23.** $6(4a+b)$ **24.** $6(6c+d)$
25. $4(2m-n)$ **26.** $4(4p-q)$ **27.** $5(3r-s)$ **28.** $5(8x-y)$
29. $7(3u-v)$ **30.** $7(5k-l)$ **31.** $2(2a+3b)$ **32.** $2(4c+5d)$
33. $3(2m+3n)$ **34.** $3(3p+7q)$ **35.** $5(2r+3s)$ **36.** $2(3u-5v)$
37. $2(5x-7y)$ **38.** $3(3b-5c)$ **39.** $5(2d-5e)$ **40.** $5(4k-7l)$
41. $2(7x+4y)$ **42.** $2(8u+5v)$

Exercise 53   *page 58*

1. 40   **2.** 60   **3.** 80   **4.** 120   **5.** 140   **6.** 220
7. 260   **8.** 280   **9.** 2000   **10.** 4000   **11.** 8000   **12.** 6000
13. 7000   **14.** 3000   **15.** 1000   **16.** 3600   **17.** 5400   **18.** 1200
19. 7800   **20.** 6400   **21.** 2800   **22.** 15 000 **23.** 16 400 **24.** 21 000
25. 9000   **26.** 9600   **27.** 9200   **28.** 9400   **29.** 8400   **30.** 8600
31. 8800   **32.** 8200   **33.** 10 200 **34.** 10 400 **35.** 11 000 **36.** 11 600
37. 58   **38.** 72   **39.** 34   **40.** 16   **41.** 70   **42.** 90
43. 94   **44.** 46   **45.** 28   **46.** 64   **47.** 2   **48.** 88
49. 70   **50.** 30   **51.** 10   **52.** 90   **53.** 55   **54.** 75

Exercise 54   *page 58*

1. $(x-4)(x+4)$ **2.** $(y-7)(y+7)$ **3.** $(z-9)(z+9)$
4. $(p-8)(p+8)$ **5.** $(q-6)(q+6)$ **6.** $(r-2)(r+2)$
7. $(a-10)(a+10)$ **8.** $(b-12)(b+12)$ **9.** $(c-11)(c+11)$
10. $(m-20)(m+20)$ **11.** $(n-30)(n+30)$ **12.** $(u-50)(u+50)$
13. $(v-40)(v+40)$ **14.** $(x-60)(x+60)$ **15.** $(y-15)(y+15)$
16. $(z-25)(z+25)$ **17.** $(a-\frac{1}{2})(b+\frac{1}{2})$ **18.** $(b-\frac{1}{3})(b+\frac{1}{3})$
19. $(c-\frac{1}{5})(c+\frac{1}{5})$ **20.** $(m-\frac{1}{4})(m+\frac{1}{4})$ **21.** $(n-\frac{1}{10})(n+\frac{1}{10})$
22. $(u-\frac{1}{6})(u+\frac{1}{6})$ **23.** $(v-\frac{1}{8})(v+\frac{1}{8})$ **24.** $(r-\frac{1}{9})(r+\frac{1}{9})$
25. $(s-\frac{1}{7})(s+\frac{1}{7})$ **26.** $(3-a)(3+a)$ **27.** $(5-b)(5+b)$
28. $(4-c)(4+c)$ **29.** $(2-d)(2+d)$ **30.** $(8-m)(8+m)$
31. $(6-n)(6+n)$ **32.** $(9-p)(9+p)$ **33.** $(1-q)(1+q)$
34. $(10-r)(10+r)$ **35.** $(12-s)(12+s)$ **36.** $(11-t)(11+t)$
37. $(30-x)(30+x)$ **38.** $(20-y)(20+y)$ **39.** $(40-z)(40+z)$
40. $(50-a)(50+a)$ **41.** $(80-b)(80+b)$ **42.** $(70-c)(70+c)$
43. $(15-d)(15+d)$ **44.** $(\frac{1}{5}-u)(\frac{1}{5}+u)$ **45.** $(\frac{1}{10}-v)(\frac{1}{10}+v)$
46. $(\frac{1}{3}-m)(\frac{1}{3}+m)$ **47.** $(\frac{1}{4}-n)(\frac{1}{4}+n)$ **48.** $(\frac{1}{2}-x)(\frac{1}{2}+x)$
49. $(\frac{1}{6}-y)(\frac{1}{6}+y)$ **50.** $(\frac{1}{12}-z)(\frac{1}{12}+z)$

Revision exercise C
page 59

1. 50 cm^2
2. 0·9 m^2
3. 6000 cm^2
4. 0·79 m^2
5. $5\frac{1}{4}$ m^2
6. £2·50
7. $5q^2 + 5q$
8. $4yz - 20y$
9. $3bc - 9b$
10. $5t^2 - 20t$
11. $2u^2 - 20u$
12. $15y - 3yz$
13. $16a - 4ab$
14. $24x - 2x^2$
15. $40m - 5m^2$
16. $rs + 6r - 3s - 18$
17. $xy + 8x - 4y - 32$
18. $uv + u - 8v - 8$
19. $mn + m - n - 1$
20. $b^2 - 3b - 4$
21. $c^2 - c - 2$
22. $m^2 + 5m - 14$
23. $n^2 + 5n - 36$
24. $p^2 + 3p - 18$
25. $q^2 + 3q - 54$
26. $r^2 + r - 12$
27. $s^2 + 7s - 8$
28. $3(4m + 3n)$
29. $3(5a + 4b)$
30. $5(5c + 3d)$
31. $2(6y - 5z)$
32. $3(5p - 2q)$
33. $3(7t - 4u)$
34. $5(4b - 3c)$
35. $5(5d - 4e)$
36. 15
37. 35
38. 95
39. 210
40. 150

BOOK 5   PART 6

Exercise 55   *page 60*

1. 65 cm^2, 150 cm^2, 720 mm^2, 360 mm^2, 4·2 m^2, 12 m^2
2. 60 cm^2, 40 cm^2, 630 mm^2, 500 mm^2, 2·7 m^2, 3 m^2
3. 12·56 cm, 15·7 cm, 31·4 cm, 62·8 mm, 47·1 mm, 314 mm
4. 12·56 cm^2, 28·26 cm^2, 3·14 cm^2, 314 mm^2, 1256 mm^2, 78·5 mm^2
5. 120 cm^3, 300 cm^3, 240 cm^3, 360 cm^3, 3000 mm^3, 1200 mm^3
6. 125·6 cm^3, 141·3 cm^3, 18·84 cm^3, 9420 mm^3, 785 mm^3, 62 800 mm^3

Exercise 56   *page 62*

1. |START| Lift receiver| Wait for dialling tone| Dial '999'| Wait until someone answers| Ask for 'Police' 'Fire Brigade' or 'Ambulance'| STOP|
2. |START| Arrive at kerb| Look right| Look left| Look right again| Cross if the road is clear| STOP|
3. |START| Lift receiver| Wait for dialling tone| Dial number required| Wait for pay tone| Insert coin| Begin conversation| STOP|
4. |START| Place the car jack in position| Raise the wheel off the ground| Remove the wheel| Place the spare wheel on| Lower the wheel to the ground| Remove the jack| STOP|
5. |START| Write letter| Address envelope| Place letter in envelope| Seal envelope| Buy a stamp| Stick the stamp on the envelope| Post letter in pillar box| STOP|
6. |START| Arrive at kerb| Press button| Wait until light shows a crossing signal| Check that all traffic has stopped| Cross road| STOP|
7. |START| Raise your arm as the bus approaches| Wait until bus stops| Board the bus| Give the driver your fare| Collect your ticket and your change| Proceed to a seat| STOP|
8. |START| Place eggs in pan| Fill pan with water until the eggs are covered| Turn on electricity| Wait until water boils| Leave eggs in the boiling water for 15 minutes| Turn off electricity and remove eggs from pan| STOP|
9. |START| Take off wheel| Remove the tyre with a lever| Place inner tube in water and inflate to locate puncture| Clean the inner tube around the puncture| Stick the patch on| Replace the inner tube and tyre on the wheel| Put the wheel back on and inflate tyre| STOP|
10. |START| Remove plug from socket| Take the back off the plug| Remove the blown fuse| Insert the new fuse| Replace the back of the plug| Replace plug in socket| Turn on the appliance and see if it works| STOP|

Exercise 57   *page 66*
1. yes, yes, no, yes, yes
2. yes, yes, yes, no, yes
3. yes, yes, no, no, yes
4. yes, yes, yes, yes, no
5. blue box
6. wall C

Exercise 60   *page 72*

1. $\begin{pmatrix} 2 \\ 4 \end{pmatrix}$
2. $\begin{pmatrix} 3 \\ 4 \end{pmatrix}$
3. $\begin{pmatrix} 2 \\ 2 \end{pmatrix}$
4. $\begin{pmatrix} 3 \\ 0 \end{pmatrix}$
5. $\begin{pmatrix} 2 \\ 1 \end{pmatrix}$
6. $\begin{pmatrix} 3 \\ -4 \end{pmatrix}$

7. $\begin{pmatrix} 1 \\ -4 \end{pmatrix}$
8. $\begin{pmatrix} 0 \\ -2 \end{pmatrix}$
9. $\begin{pmatrix} -2 \\ 3 \end{pmatrix}$
10. $\begin{pmatrix} -4 \\ 3 \end{pmatrix}$
11. $\begin{pmatrix} -3 \\ 3 \end{pmatrix}$
12. $\begin{pmatrix} -3 \\ -1 \end{pmatrix}$

13. $\begin{pmatrix} -6 \\ -1 \end{pmatrix}$
14. $\begin{pmatrix} -2 \\ -4 \end{pmatrix}$
15. $\begin{pmatrix} -5 \\ -5 \end{pmatrix}$
16. $\begin{pmatrix} -6 \\ -3 \end{pmatrix}$

Exercise 64   *page 79*
1. a, b, −b, −a
2. a, −b, b, −a
3. −a, b, −b, a
4. −a, −b, b, a
5. a, b, −b, −a
6. a, −b, b, −a
7. −a, b, −b, a
8. −a, b, b, a

Exercise 65   *page 80*
1. 2a, b, −2a, −b
2. 3a, b, −3a, −b
3. a, 2b, −a, −2b
4. 2b, 3a, −2b, −3a
5. 5a, 3b, −5a, −3b
6. 7b, 4a, −7b, −4a
7. 3b, 2a, −3b, −2a
8. 5b, 2a, −5b, −2a
9. −2a, −b, 2a, b
10. −4a, −b, 4a, b
11. −4a, −3b, 4a, 3b
12. −5a, −2b, 5a, 2b

Exercise 66   *page 81*
1. x + z, y + z, x − y
2. u + w, v + w, u − v
3. p + r, q + r, p − q, q − p
4. s + u, t + u, s − t, t − s
5. p + q, r + q, p − r
6. u + v, w + v, u − w
7. x + y, z + y, x − z, z − x
8. r − t, r − s, s − t, t − s
9. x − z, x − y, y − z, z − y
10. p − r, p − q, q − r, r − q, r − p
11. u + w, u + v, −v + w, −v − u
12. x + z, x + y, −y + z, −y − x

Exercise 67   *page 83*
1. $\overrightarrow{PR}, \overrightarrow{QP}, O, \overrightarrow{RP}, \overrightarrow{PQ}$
2. $\overrightarrow{LN}, \overrightarrow{ML}, O, \overrightarrow{NL}, \overrightarrow{LM}$
3. $\overrightarrow{XZ}, \overrightarrow{ZY}, O, \overrightarrow{ZX}, \overrightarrow{YZ}$
4. $\overrightarrow{AC}, \overrightarrow{CB}, O, \overrightarrow{CA}, \overrightarrow{BC}$
5. $\overrightarrow{UW}, \overrightarrow{VU}, \overrightarrow{UV}, O$
6. $\overrightarrow{BD}, \overrightarrow{CB}, \overrightarrow{BC}, O$
7. $\overrightarrow{NP}, \overrightarrow{NM}, \overrightarrow{MN}, O$
8. $\overrightarrow{XZ}, \overrightarrow{ZX}, \overrightarrow{ZY}, O$
9. $\overrightarrow{PR}, \overrightarrow{RP}, \overrightarrow{RQ}, O$
10. $\overrightarrow{UW}, \overrightarrow{WU}, \overrightarrow{WV}, O$
11. $\overrightarrow{BC}, \overrightarrow{CB}, \overrightarrow{BA}, O$
12. $\overrightarrow{VW}, \overrightarrow{WV}, \overrightarrow{VU}, O$

Exercise 68   *page 84*
1. $\frac{3}{5}, \frac{3}{10}, \frac{1}{10}$
2. $\frac{1}{5}, \frac{1}{2}, \frac{3}{10}$
3. $\frac{1}{6}, \frac{1}{3}, \frac{1}{12}, \frac{5}{12}$
4. $\frac{1}{2}, \frac{2}{5}, \frac{1}{10}$
5. $\frac{2}{3}, \frac{1}{4}, \frac{1}{12}$
6. $\frac{1}{3}, \frac{1}{4}, \frac{1}{6}, \frac{1}{4}, \frac{7}{12}, \frac{5}{12}$
7. $\frac{1}{2}, \frac{2}{3}, \frac{1}{3}$
8. $\frac{1}{2}, \frac{1}{2}, 1$

Exercise 69   *page 86*
1. $\frac{1}{3}, \frac{2}{3}, \frac{1}{9}, \frac{1}{9}, \frac{1}{9}$
2. $\frac{1}{3}, \frac{2}{3}, \frac{4}{9}$
3. $\frac{1}{3}, \frac{4}{9}, \frac{4}{9}, \frac{1}{9}$
4. $\frac{1}{3}, \frac{4}{9}, \frac{1}{9}$
5. $\frac{1}{9}, \frac{4}{9}, \frac{4}{9}, \frac{4}{9}$
6. $\frac{4}{9}, \frac{1}{9}, \frac{4}{9}$
7. $\frac{5}{9}, \frac{4}{9}, \frac{1}{9}$
8. $\frac{5}{9}, \frac{4}{9}, 1$

Exercise 70   *page 87*
1. $\frac{1}{3}, \frac{2}{3}, \frac{1}{3}$.
2. $\frac{1}{3}, \frac{2}{3}, \frac{2}{3}$
3. $\frac{1}{3}, \frac{2}{3}, 1$
4. $\frac{1}{3}, \frac{1}{3}$
5. $\frac{1}{3}, \frac{2}{3}$
6. $\frac{1}{3}, \frac{1}{3}$

7. $\frac{1}{3}$, $\frac{2}{3}$ 8. $\frac{1}{2}$, $\frac{1}{3}$

Revision exercise D
page 88

1. $60°$, $40°$, $30°$, $20°$, $35°$, $55°$
2. $60°$, $108°$, $135°$, $144°$, $150°$, $156°$
3. £12, £18, £33, £54, £630, £225
4. £80, £60, £45, £125, £20, £6
5. Entrance hall   6. Mr. Scott's yard

7. $\frac{1}{4}$, $\frac{1}{3}$, $\frac{1}{6}$, $\frac{1}{4}$, $\frac{1}{3}$ 8. $\frac{1}{4}$, $\frac{1}{8}$, $\frac{1}{4}$, $\frac{3}{8}$, $\frac{1}{2}$, $\frac{1}{4}$, $\frac{1}{4}$ 9. $\frac{4}{9}$, $\frac{4}{9}$

10. $\frac{1}{4}$, $\frac{1}{4}$, $\frac{1}{4}$, $\frac{9}{16}$, 1   11. $\frac{1}{2}$, $\frac{1}{6}$, $\frac{1}{6}$, $\frac{1}{2}$ 12. $\frac{1}{2}$, $\frac{1}{6}$, $\frac{1}{6}$

answers

BOOK 6   PART 1

Exercise 1 *page 1*

1. +£3·50	2. +£6·50	3. +£4·50	4. −£2·50	5. −£3·50
6. +£2·50	7. +£3·50	8. +£7·50	9. −£3·50	10. −£4·50
11. −£4·25	12. −£2·75	13. +£6·25	14. +£6·25	15. +£4·75
16. +£2·75	17. −£3·25	18. −£3·75	19. +£4·25	20. +£2·75
21. £1·75	22. £22·50	23. £35	24. £250	25. £3750

Exercise 2 *page 1*

1. +20p	2. +20p	3. +60p	4. −£2	5. −£1
6. −£1	7. +25p	8. +£2·50	9. +£4·50	10. −75p
11. −60p	12. +£1	13. +25p	14. −£6	15. −60p
16. +£1·50	17. +30p	18. +24p	19. −72p	20. −48p

Exercise 3 *page 2*

1. (a)	2. (c)	3. (b)	4. (a)	5. (c)	6. (a)
7. (b)	8. (c)	9. (a)	10. (b)		

Exercise 4 *page 2*

1. 20%	2. 25%	3. 5%	4. 30%	5. 15%	6. 25%
7. 5%	8. 20%	9. 30%	10. 15%	11. 25%	12. 20%
13. 30%	14. 5%	15. 15%	16. 20%	17. 30%	18. 15%
19. 25%	20. 5%				

Exercise 5 *page 3*

1. +20%	2. +25%	3. +15%	4. −10%	5 −20%	6. −5%
7. +10%	8. +25%	9. +15%	10. −25%	11. −10%	12. +20%
13. +5%	14. −15%	15. −5%	16. +10%	17. +25%	18. +5%
19. −20%	20. −25%				

Exercise 6 *page 3*

1. $\frac{1}{3}$	2. $\frac{2}{3}$	3. $\frac{1}{2}$	4. $\frac{1}{6}$	5. $\frac{1}{5}$	6. $\frac{4}{5}$	7. $\frac{2}{5}$	8. $\frac{3}{5}$
9. $\frac{1}{10}$	10. $\frac{3}{10}$	11. $\frac{9}{10}$	12. $\frac{1}{12}$	13. $\frac{5}{12}$	14. $\frac{11}{12}$	15. $\frac{3}{4}$	16. $\frac{1}{15}$
17. $\frac{2}{15}$	18. $\frac{1}{20}$	19. $\frac{3}{20}$	20. $\frac{9}{20}$				

Exercise 7 *page 4*

1. 50 km/h	2. 60 km/h	3. 55 km/h	4. 84 km/h
5. 63 km/h	6. 82 km/h	7. 134 km/h	8. 118 km/h
9. 103 km/h	10. 105 km/h	11. 40 km/h	12. 80 km/h
13. 60 km/h	14. 100 km/h	15. 50 km/h	16. 72 km/h
17. 120 km/h	18. 80 km/h	19. 40 km/h	20. 120 km/h

Exercise 8 *page 5*

1. 100 km/h	2. 48 km/h	3. 72 km/h	4. 60 km/h
5. 84 km/h	6. 100 km/h	7. 75 km/h	8. 96 km/h
9. 54 km/h	10. 72 km/h	11. 48 km/h	12. 70 km/h
13. 135 km/h	14. 108 km/h	15. 92 km/h	16. 140 km/h
17. 60 km/h	18. 42 km/h	19. 39 km/h	20. 32 km/h

Exercise 9 *page 6*

1. 240 km	**2.** 360 km	**3.** 450 km	**4.** 360 km	**5.** 170 km
6. 385 km	**7.** 500 km	**8.** 423 km	**9.** 540 km	**10.** 75 km
11. 200 km	**12.** 180 km	**13.** 200 km	**14.** 70 km	**15.** 180 km
16. 440 km	**17.** 16 km	**18.** 90 km	**19.** 105 km	**20.** 90 km
21. 105 km	**22.** 210 km	**23.** 162 km	**24.** 120 km	**25.** 80 km
26. 147 km	**27.** 24 km	**28.** 63 km	**29.** 16 km	**30.** 60 km
31. 300 km	**32.** 375 km	**33.** 846 km	**34.** 192 km	**35.** 231 km
36. 80 km	**37.** 63 km	**38.** 36 km	**39.** 18 km	**40.** 360 km

Exercise 10 *page 7*

1. 3 h	**2.** 4 h	**3.** 8 h	**4.** 5 h	**5.** 6 h	**6.** 7 h
7. 4 h	**8.** 8 h	**9.** 5 h	**10.** 3 h	**11.** 6 h	**12.** 4 h
13. 7 h	**14.** 9 h	**15.** 1 h 30 min		**16.** 2 h 30 min	
17. 3 h 30 min	**18.** 4 h 30 min	**19.** 1 h 15 min	**20.** 1 h 45 min		
21. 2 h 15 min	**22.** 2 h 45 min	**23.** 1 h 20 min	**24.** 1 h 40 min		
25. 2 h 20 min	**26.** 2 h 40 min	**27.** 15 min	**28.** 45 min		
29. 20 min	**30.** 40 min	**31.** 5 h	**32.** 6 h		
33. 9 h	**34.** 4 h 30 min	**35.** 2 h 30 min	**36.** 1 h 45 min		
37. 1 h 40 min	**38.** 2 h 15 min	**39.** 15 min	**40.** 40 min		

Exercise 11 *page 8*

1. 9   **2.** 36   **3.** 4   **4.** 81   **5.** 0·49

6. 0·16   **7.** 0·64   **8.** 0·01   **9.** 1·21   **10.** $\frac{1}{4}$

11. $\frac{1}{16}$ **12.** $\frac{1}{25}$ **13.** $\frac{1}{144}$ **14.** $\frac{9}{16}$ **15.** $\frac{9}{25}$

16. $\frac{9}{64}$ **17.** $\frac{49}{64}$ **18.** $\frac{81}{100}$ **19.** $\frac{25}{144}$ **20.** $\frac{121}{144}$

21. $1\frac{7}{9}$ **22.** $1\frac{11}{25}$ **23.** $3\frac{6}{25}$ **24.** $6\frac{1}{4}$ **25.** $20\frac{1}{4}$

Exercise 12 *page 8*

1. 8   **2.** 5   **3.** 10   **4.** 4   **5.** 1   **6.** $\frac{1}{3}$ **7.** $\frac{1}{6}$ **8.** $\frac{1}{8}$

9. $\frac{1}{10}$ **10.** $\frac{2}{3}$ **11.** $\frac{2}{5}$ **12.** $\frac{4}{5}$ **13.** $\frac{5}{6}$ **14.** $\frac{5}{8}$ **15.** $\frac{3}{10}$ **16.** $\frac{7}{10}$

17. $\frac{7}{12}$ **18.** 0·5   **19.** 0·6   **20.** 0·9   **21.** 1·2   **22.** $1\frac{2}{5}$ **23.** $1\frac{2}{3}$ **24.** $1\frac{3}{5}$

25. $1\frac{3}{4}$ **26.** $2\frac{1}{5}$ **27.** $2\frac{1}{3}$ **28.** $2\frac{1}{4}$ **29.** $3\frac{1}{3}$ **30.** $3\frac{1}{2}$

Exercise 13 *page 9*

1. 400	**2.** 169	**3.** 196	**4.** 324	**5.** 484	**6.** 676
7. 729	**8.** 841	**9.** 961	**10.** 1600	**11.** 3600	**12.** 4900
13. 1225	**14.** 4225	**15.** 5625	**16.** 10 000	**17.** 1156	**18.** 1681
19. 2304	**20.** 3136	**21.** 3969	**22.** 6084	**23.** 8281	**24.** 9604

Exercise 14 *page 9*

1. 30	**2.** 15	**3.** 25	**4.** 16	**5.** 17	**6.** 19	**7.** 21	**8.** 23
9. 24	**10.** 28	**11.** 50	**12.** 80	**13.** 90	**14.** 45	**15.** 55	**16.** 85
17. 32	**18.** 44	**19.** 54	**20.** 61	**21.** 72	**22.** 84	**23.** 81	**24.** 99

Exercise 15 *page 10*

1. 25	**2.** 26	**3.** 34	**4.** 50	**5.** 29	**6.** 53	**7.** 41	**8.** 61
9. 37	**10.** 100	**11.** 8	**12.** 12	**13.** 15	**14.** 60	**15.** 24	**16.** 40
17. 60	**18.** 80	**19.** 70	**20.** 28				

Exercise 16 *page 10*

1. 72 m   **2.** 104 cm   **3.** 132 cm   **4.** 300 cm   **5.** no, the error is +4 m

Exercise 17 *page 11*

1. 3721 cm^2 **2.** 75 m, 5625 m^2 **3.** 24 m, 6 m, 36 m^2

4. 100 cm, 96 cm, 24 cm, 3 cm, 9 cm^2, 576 cm^2

5. 40 cm, 1600 cm^2 **6.** 2025 cm^2 **7.** 5400 cm^2

BOOK 6   PART 2

Exercise 18 *page 12*
1. 12 mm 16 mm 20 mm
2. 16 mm 30 mm 34 mm
3. 20 mm 21 mm 29 mm
4. 9 mm 40 mm 41 mm
5. 11 mm 60 mm 61 mm
6. 12 mm 35 mm 37 mm

Exercise 19 *page 12*
1. 81 1600 1681 1681
2. 121 3600 3721 3721
3. 144 1225 1369 1369
4. 144 256 400 400
5. 400 441 841 841
6. 25 144 169 169
7. 256 900 1156 1156
8. 900 1600 2500 2500
9. 169 7056 7225 7225
10. 784 9216 10 000 10 000

Exercise 20 *page 13*
1. 15 cm
2. 17 cm
3. 26 cm
4. 40 cm
5. 50 mm
6. 100 cm
7. 90 cm
8. 75 mm
9. 65 mm
10. 45 mm
11. 75 cm
12. 65 cm
13. 85 cm
14. 1 m
15. $\frac{1}{2}$ m

Exercise 21 *page 14*
1. 7 cm
2. 20 cm
3. 40 cm
4. 80 mm
5. 16 mm
6. 45 mm
7. 36 cm
8. 35 cm
9. $1\frac{1}{5}$ m
10. $\frac{2}{5}$ m
11. 20 cm
12. 15 cm
13. 18 cm
14. 40 mm
15. 30 mm
16. 70 mm
17. 21 cm
18. 45 cm
19. 48 cm
20. $1\frac{1}{5}$ m

Exercise 22 *page 14*
1. $2\frac{1}{2}$ m
2. 96 m
3. 30 mm
4. 25 mm
5. 10 cm

Exercise 23 *page 15*
1. (c)
2. (b)
3. (a)
4. (b)
5. (c)
6. (a)
7. (c)
8. (b)
9. (c)
10. (a)

Exercise 24 *page 19*
1. (a) and (b)
2. (b) and (c)
3. (b) and (c)
4. (a) and (c)
5. (a) and (c)
6. (b) and (c)
7. (a) and (b)
8. (b) and (c)
9. (a) and (b)
10. (a) and (c)
11. (a) and (b)
12. (b) and (c)
13. (b) and (c)
14. (a) and (c)
15. (b) and (c)

Exercise 25 *page 23*
1. 7 cm from any vertex
2. $6\frac{1}{4}$ cm from any vertex
3. 7 cm from any vertex
4. 8 cm from any vertex
6. 8 cm from any vertex
8. 7 cm from any vertex
10. 5 cm from Q

Revision exercise A
page 24
1. 20 cm
2. 15 cm
3. 13 cm
4. 5 cm
5. 12 cm
6. $60°, 30°, 30°, 60°$. They are similar.

BOOK 6   PART 3

Exercise 26 *page 25*

1.

	A	B	C	D	E	F
x	−2	−1	0	1	2	3
y	−7	−5	−3	−1	1	3

2.

	A	B	C	D	E	F
x	−3	−2	−1	0	1	2
y	−2	0	2	4	6	8

3.

	A	B	C	D	E	F
x	−2	−1	0	1	2	3
y	−8	−6	−4	−2	0	2

4.

	A	B	C	D	E	F	G
x	−3	−2	−1	0	1	2	3
y	−8	−5	−2	1	4	7	10

Exercise 28   *page 27*

1. $y = 1, 3, 5, 7$ and 9
2. $y = 4, 6, 8, 10$ and 12
3. $y = -5, -1, 3, 7$ and 11
4. $y = -7, -3, 1, 5$ and 9
5. $y = -9, -5, -1, 3$ and 7
6. $y = -11, -7, -3, 1$ and 5
7. $y = -8, -3, 2, 7$ and 12

Exercise 30   *page 30*

1.
	A	B	C	D	E	F
x	-2	-1	0	1	$1\frac{1}{2}$	2
y	4	1	0	1	$2\frac{1}{4}$	4

2.
	A	B	C	D	E	F
x	-2	-1	0	1	$1\frac{1}{2}$	2
y	3	0	-1	0	$1\frac{1}{4}$	3

3.
	A	B	C	D	E	F	G
x	-3	-2	-1	0	1	2	3
y	3	-2	-5	-6	-5	-2	3

4.
	A	B	C	D	E	F	G	H	I
x	-2	$-1\frac{1}{2}$	-1	$-\frac{1}{2}$	0	$\frac{1}{2}$	1	$1\frac{1}{2}$	2
y	$3\frac{3}{4}$	2	$\frac{3}{4}$	0	$-\frac{1}{4}$	0	$\frac{3}{4}$	2	$3\frac{3}{4}$

5.
	A	B	C	D	E	F
x	-2	-1	0	$\frac{1}{2}$	1	2
y	-3	0	1	$\frac{3}{4}$	0	-3

6.
	A	B	C	D	E	F	G
x	-2	-1	0	$\frac{1}{2}$	1	$1\frac{1}{2}$	2
y	0	3	4	$3\frac{3}{4}$	3	$1\frac{3}{4}$	0

Exercise 32   *page 33*

1. $y = 10, 5, 2, 1, 2, 5$ and 10
2. $y = 12, 7, 4, 3, 4, 7$ and 12
3. $y = 15, 10, 7, 6, 7, 10$ and 15
4. $y = 2, -3, -6, -7, -6, -3$ and 2
5. $y = 0, -5, -8, -9, -8, -5$ and 0
6. $y = -1, 4, 7, 8, 7, 4$ and -1
7. $y = -5, 0, 3, 4, 3, 0$ and -5
8. $y = -8, -3, 0, 1, 0, -3$ and -8

Exercise 33   *page 35*

1. $y = 5, 0, -3, -4, -3, 0$ and 5
2. $y = 4, 0, -2, -2, 0$ and 4
3. $y = 6, 0, -4, -6, -6, -4, 0$ and 6
4. $y = 6, 2, 0, 0, 2$ and 6
5. $y = -5, 0, 3, 4, 3, 0$ and -5
6. $y = -3, 0, 1, 0,$ and -3
7. $y = -4, 0, 2, 2, 0$ and -4
8. $y = 3, 0, -1, 0$ and 3
9. $y = 4, 0, -2, -2, 0$ and 4
10. $y = 6, 2, 0, 0, 2$ and 6

Revision exercise B
page 35

1. £15, £35; 5 years, 1 year
2. 11 cm, 23 cm; 4 cm, 6 cm
3. 12 cm, 20 cm; 5 cm, 1 cm
4. 13 cm, 19 cm; 100 g, 20 g
5. 9, 25, 81

BOOK 6   PART 4

Exercise 34   *page 37*

1. 36 cm² 　 2. 14 cm² 　 3. 16 mm² 　 4. 15 mm² 　 5. 14 mm²
6. 24 cm² 　 7. 20 cm² 　 8. 12 cm² 　 9. 15 cm² 　 10. 90 mm²
11. 30 mm² 　 12. 45 mm² 　 13. 35 cm² 　 14. 12 cm² 　 15. 2 cm²
16. 12·3 cm² 　 17. 54 cm²

Exercise 35 *page 38*
1. 60°   2. 90°   3. 45°   4. 30°   5. 40°
6. 72°   7. 120°   8. 150°   9. 135°   10. 240°
11. 300°   12. 270°   13. 108°   14. 210°   15. 24°

Exercise 36 *page 38*
1. 154 cm²   2. 77 cm²   3. 1925 mm²   4. 3080 mm²   5. 154 cm²
6. 231 cm²   7. 1·57 cm²   8. 4·71 cm²   9. 3·14 cm²   10. 9·42 cm²
11. 157 mm²   12. 4·71 mm²   13. 350 cm²   14. 3828 cm²

Exercise 37 *page 39*
1. 480 cm³, 450 cm³, 5 m³   2. 200 cm³, 7200 mm³, 18 m³
3. 60 mm³, 2500 mm³, 35 m³   4. 120 cm³, 7·5 m³, $\frac{3}{4}$ m³
5. 1540 cm³, 88 000 mm³, 7·7 m³   6. 6160 mm³, 22 m³, 44 mm³

Exercise 38 *page 40*
1. 24 cm³   2. 300 000 cm³   3. 24 m³   4. 1440 m³   5. 98 m³
6. 1540 m³   7. 3850 cm³   8. 51 240 cm³   9. 3325 m³   10. 100·5 cm³

Exercise 39 *page 42*
1. 10 000 *l*, 9000 *l*, 7000 *l*   2. 2000 *l*, 27 000 *l*, 18 000 *l*
3. 48 *l*, 56 *l*, 54 *l*   4. 10 *l*, 20 *l*, 14 *l*

Exercise 40 *page 42*
1. 22 m³, 22 000 *l*   2. 8·8 m³, 8800 *l*
3. 1650 cm³, 1650 m*l*, yes   4. 6600 cm³, 6600 m*l*, 1320
5. 13 200 cm³, 13 200 m*l*, 240   6. 44 000 cm³, 44 *l*, 220
7. 11 000 cm³, 11 *l*, yes

BOOK 6   PART 5

Exercise 41 *page 43*
1. 3	2. 2	3. 4	4. 4	5. 2	6. 3	7. 4	8. 5
9. 3	10. 6	11. 4	12. 4	13. 6	14. 3	15. 4	16. 5
17. 8	18. 3	19. 7	20. 4				

Exercise 42 *page 43*
1. 3	2. 2	3. 4	4. 5	5. 1	6. 4	7. 6	8. 3
9. 2	10. 5	11. 5	12. 7	13. 2	14. 6	15. 8	16. −2
17. −4	18. −3	19. −5	20. −6	21. 2	22. 5	23. 4	24. 7
25. 1	26. −3	27. −2	28. −6	29. −5	30. −12		

Exercise 43 *page 43*
1. 2	2. 5	3. 1	4. 3	5. 7	6. 2	7. 5	8. 4
9. 6	10. 1	11. 7	12. 8	13. 2	14. 4	15. 3	16. 5
17. 9	18. 2	19. 2	20. 5	21. 3	22. 8	23. 5	24. 6
25. 2	26. 4	27. 3	28. 1	29. 5	30. 6		

Exercise 44 *page 44*
1. 2	2. 4	3. 3	4. 5	5. 7	6. 12	7. 5	8. 5
9. 6	10. 3	11. 4	12. 2	13. 3	14. 1	15. 5	16. 1
17. 2	18. 4	19. 6	20. 9	21. 8	22. 10	23. 9	24. 11
25. 4	26. 6	27. 5	28. 4	29. 5	30. 1		

Exercise 45 *page 44*
1. 3	2. 2	3. 1	4. 4	5. 3	6. 3	7. 5	8. 2
9. 1	10. 3	11. 5	12. 4	13. 3	14. 4	15. 5	16. 1
17. 8	18. 9	19. 6	20. 7	21. 8	22. 24	23. 2	24. 4
25. 5	26. 2						

Exercise 46 *page 45*

1. 25	2. 9	3. 100	4. 16	5. 64
6. 8	7. 27	8. 1000	9. 16	10. 81
11. 625	12. 32	13. 100 000	14. 72	15. 128
16. 64	17. 144	18. 100	19. 200	20. 225
21. 400	22. 1600	23. 3200	24. 900	25. 2700
26. 1600	27. 2500	28. 12 500	29. 108	30. 216
31. 256	32. 512	33. 576	34. 500	35. 1125
36. 4000	37. 16 000	38. 32 000	39. 9000	40. 27 000
41. 16 000	42. 25 000	43. 324	44. 648	45. 40 000
46. 320 000	47. 90 000	48. 270 000	49. 160 000	50. 250 000
51. 400 000	52. 800 000	53. 3 200 000	54. 900 000	55. 2 700 000
56. 1 600 000	57. 2 500 000	58. 4	59. 2	60. 8
61. 1	62. 25	63. 4	64. 20	65. 16
66. 4	67. 2	68. 250	69. 125	70. 40
71. 8	72. 200	73. 2	74. 1	75. 27
76. 9	77. 3	78. 81	79. 125	80. 25
81. 625	82. 100	83. 10	84. 9	85. 27
86. 25	87. 5	88. 25	89. 4	90. 16

Exercise 47 *page 46*

1. a^3	2. b^5	3. c^2	4. d^6	5. e^7	6. p^5
7. $2q^5$	8. $4r^5$	9. $10s^5$	10. t^6	11. $7u^6$	12. $12v^6$
13. a^4	14. $6b^4$	15. $24c^4$	16. m^7	17. $8n^7$	18. $20p^7$
19. d^6	20. $4e^6$	21. $18f^6$	22. s^5	23. $6u^5$	24. $35v^5$
25. a^7	26. $12c^7$	27. $16d^7$	28. p^6	29. $11q^6$	30. $30r^6$
31. t^4	32. $5u^4$	33. $28v^4$	34. m^3	35. $9n^3$	36. $11p^3$
37. $40q^3$	38. $20d^2$	39. $5e^2$	40. $12f^2$		

Exercise 48 *page 47*

1. a^2	2. $5b^2$	3. $4c^2$	4. p^3	5. $3p^3$	6. $2r^3$
7. t^4	8. $4u^4$	9. $3v^4$	10. m^5	11. $5n^5$	12. a^2
13. $8b^2$	14. $4c^2$	15. d^3	16. $11e^3$	17. $2f^3$	18. y^4
19. $4z^4$	20. p^2	21. $7q^2$	22. $7r^2$	23. m^3	24. $6n^3$
25. t	26. $6u$	27. $3v$	28. p^4	29. $9q^4$	30. $3r^4$
31. a^2	32. $4b^2$	33. $5c^2$	34. r	35. $10s$	36. $5t$
37. 1	38. 6	39. 3	40. t^2	41. $8u^2$	42. $3v^2$
43. 1	44. 13	45. 8	46. p	47. $9q$	48. $5r$
49. 1	50. 8				

Exercise 49 *page 48*

1. 5, 3	2. 6, 2	3. 7, 1	4. 7, 2	5. 6, 3	6. 8, 1
7. 5, 2	8. 6, 1	9. 4, 1	10. 3, 2	11. 3, 1	12. 5, 1
13. 2, 1	14. 8, 2	15. 6, 4	16. 7, 3	17. 9, 3	18. 11, 1
19. 15, 5	20. 12, 8				

Exercise 50 *page 48*

1. 3, 1	2. 4, 2	3. 3, 2	4. 4, 1	5. 2, 1	6. 4, 3
7. 3, 2	8. 2, 7	9. 5, 2	10. 6, 1	11. 8, 2	12. 10, 3
13. 3, 2	14. 2, 4	15. 3, 1	16. 4, 2	17. 2, 3	18. 3, 6
19. 1, 4	20. 2, 7	21. 1, 3	22. 2, 5	23. 2, 3	24. 2, 5
25. 1, 4	26. 2, 9	27. 3, 10	28. 1, 2	29. 2, 4	30. 3, 6

Exercise 51 *page 49*

1. 3, 2	2. 2, 4	3. 3, 5	4. 4, 10	5. 4, 2	6. 2, 5
7. 3, 4	8. 6, 3	9. 2, 6	10. 4, 5	11. 3, 5	12. 2, 3
13. 4, 3	14. 2, 4	15. 3, 1	16. 4, 3	17. 5, 2	18. 4, 1
19. 6, 5	20. 3, 4	21. 3, 2	22. 4, 5	23. 3, 1	24. 6, 2
25. 10, 3	26. 9, 2	27. 4, 2	28. 2, 3	29. 4, 3	30. 3, 5

Revision exercise C
page 50

1. 3 cm   **2.** 9 cm   **3.** 5 cm   **4.** 75 m   **5.** 14 km   **6.** 30 kg
7. 45, 35   **8.** 55 kg, 40 kg   **9.** 90 km, 60 km   **10.** 12 cm, 9 cm

---

BOOK 6   PART 6

Exercise 52   *page 52*

1. (a) 2 and 5   (b) 1   (c) 3 and 4
2. (a) 3   (b) 1 and 2   (c) 4 and 5
3. (a) 1 and 5   (b) 2 and 3   (c) 4
4. (a) 1 and 5   (b) 3 and 4   (c) 2
5. (a) 3   (b) 2 and 4   (c) 1 and 5
6. (a) 1 and 5   (b) 4   (c) 2 and 3
7. (a) 2   (b) 3 and 4   (c) 1 and 5
8. (a) 1 and 2   (b) 4   (c) 3 and 5
9. (a) 1 and 5   (b) 4   (c) 2 and 3

Exercise 53   *page 54*

1. 3 cm, 6 cm, $\frac{1}{2}$ **2.** 5 cm, 10 cm, $\frac{1}{2}$ **3.** 4 cm, 8 cm, $\frac{1}{2}$
4. 2 cm, 4 cm, $\frac{1}{2}$

Exercise 54   *page 55*

1. $\frac{AC}{AB}$ **2.** $\frac{XZ}{XY}$ **3.** $\frac{PR}{PQ}$ **4.** $\frac{LN}{LM}$ **5.** $\frac{UW}{UV}$ **6.** $\frac{BD}{BC}$

7. $\frac{ST}{SR}$ **8.** $\frac{LM}{LK}$ **9.** $\frac{EF}{ED}$ **10.** $\frac{UV}{UT}$ **11.** $\frac{CD}{CB}$ **12.** $\frac{RS}{RQ}$

13. (c)   **14.** (b)   **15.** (b)   **16.** (a)   **17.** (a)   **18.** (c)

Exercise 55   *page 58*

1. $\frac{BC}{BA}$ **2.** $\frac{LM}{LK}$ **3.** $\frac{VW}{VU}$ **4.** $\frac{YZ}{YX}$ **5.** $\frac{MN}{ML}$ **6.** $\frac{QR}{QP}$

7. $\frac{DF}{DE}$ **8.** $\frac{TV}{TU}$ **9.** $\frac{BD}{BC}$ **10.** $\frac{QS}{QR}$ **11.** $\frac{KM}{KL}$ **12.** $\frac{RT}{RS}$

13. (b)   **14.** (c)   **15.** (a)   **16.** (b)   **17.** (b)   **18.** (c)

Exercise 56   *page 60*

1. $\frac{AC}{BC}$ **2.** $\frac{LN}{MN}$ **3.** $\frac{XZ}{YZ}$ **4.** $\frac{PR}{QR}$ **5.** $\frac{UW}{VW}$ **6.** $\frac{BD}{CD}$

7. $\frac{UV}{TV}$Q   **8.** $\frac{EF}{DF}$ **9.** $\frac{ST}{RT}$ **10.** $\frac{RS}{QS}$ **11.** $\frac{MN}{LN}$ **12.** $\frac{CD}{BD}$

13. (b)   **14.** (a)   **15.** (c)   **16.** (a)   **17.** (b)   **18.** (b)

Exercise 57   *page 63*

1. 0·342   **2.** 0·500   **3.** 0·766   **4.** 0·866   **5.** 0·259
6. 0·574   **7.** 0·906   **8.** 0·996   **9.** 0·087   **10.** 0·139
11. 0·208   **12.** 0·454   **13.** 0·656   **14.** 0·914   **15.** 0·993
16. 10°   **17.** 40°   **18.** 70°   **19.** 80°   **20.** 25°
21. 45°   **22.** 55°   **23.** 75°   **24.** 3°   **25.** 9°
26. 22°   **27.** 38°   **28.** 59°   **29.** 77°   **30.** 84°

Exercise 58   *page 64*

1. 2·828 cm	2. 3·256 cm	3. 1·456 mm	4. 4·386 mm
5. 2·853 m	6. 7·368 m	7. 1·719 mm	8. 3·605 mm
9. 2·457 cm	10. 4·17 cm	11. 3·83 cm	12. 1·94 cm
13. 2·25 m	14. 1·99 m	15. 2·87 cm	16. 1·026 cm
17. 2·572 cm	18. 1·176 cm	19. 0·945 mm	20. 0·61 mm

Exercise 59   *page 65*

1. 4·854 cm	2. 1·812 cm	3. 1·806 cm	4. 2·472 mm
5. 1·955 mm	6. 3·564 m	7. 8·649 m	8. 5·484 cm
9. 2·157 cm	10. 2·464 cm	11. 4·36 mm	12. 5·25 mm
13. 3·94 cm	14. 1·51 cm	15. 1·8 cm	16. 1·692 m
17. 1·312 m	18. 2·229 m	19. 0·556 cm	20. 0·78 cm

Exercise 60   *page 66*

1. 40°	2. 25°	3. 45°	4. 60°	5. 75°	6. 70°
7. 82°	8. 66°	9. 58°	10. 36°	11. 20°	12. 9°
13. 80°	14. 31°	15. 6°	16. 61°	17. 13°	18. 22°
19. 61°	20. 4°				

Exercise 61   *page 68*

1. 50°	2. 35°	3. 80°	4. 65°	5. 55°	6. 76°
7. 30°	8. 43°	9. 71°	10. 38°	11. 21°	12. 10°
13. 49°	14. 33°	15. 29°	16. 22°	17. 61°	18. 13°

Exercise 62   *page 69*

1. 0·985	2. 0·866	3. 0·500	4. 0·342	5. 0·966
6. 0·906	7. 0·707	8. 0·423	9. 0·259	10. 0·993
11. 0·988	12. 0·875	13. 0·669	14. 0·469	15. 0·070
16. 20°	17. 40°	18. 50°	19. 80°	20. 5°
21. 35°	22. 55°	23. 85°	24. 4°	25. 12°
26. 24°	27. 33°	28. 56°	29. 71°	30. 88°

Exercise 63   *page 70*

1. 2·427 cm	2. 5·436 cm	3. 5·418 cm	4. 1·236 m
5. 1·173 m	6. 5·526 mm	7. 4·805 mm	8. 1·438 cm
9. 4·312 cm	10. 4·53 cm	11. 1·75 cm	12. 7·88 mm
13. 2·18 mm	14. 1·35 mm	15. 1·46 mm	16. 1·364 m
17. 1·887 m	18. 1·816 m	19. 0·936 cm	20. 0·348 cm

Exercise 64   *page 71*

1. 2·442 cm	2. 5·656 cm	3. 1·456 cm	4. 2·924 m
5. 4·455 m	6. 5·706 mm	7. 1·337 mm	8. 4·635 mm
9. 6·552 cm	10. 3·656 cm	11. 2·91 cm	12. 2·94 cm
13. 1·39 m	14. 1·5 m	15. 5·97 m	16. 2·802 cm
17. 1·576 cm	18. 0·968 cm	19. 0·735 mm	20. 0·312 mm

Exercise 65   *page 72*

1. 40°	2. 35°	3. 55°	4. 25°	5. 10°	6. 20°
7. 60°	8. 73°	9. 49°	10. 38°	11. 21°	12. 83°
13. 57°	14. 61°	15. 41°	16. 68°	17. 77°	18. 29°
19. 68°	20. 88°				

Exercise 66   *page 73*

1. 30°	2. 50°	3. 65°	4. 45°	5. 15°	6. 8°
7. 76°	8. 69°	99. 55°	10. 32°	11. 58°	12. 14°
13. 59°	14. 10°	15. 84°	16. 29°	17. 68°	18. 77°
19. 29°	20. 86°				

Exercise 67   *page 75*

1. 0·577	2. 0·176	3. 0·268	4. 0·700	5. 0·306
6. 0·532	7. 0·810	8. 0·900	9. 1·00	10. 1·19
11. 2·14	12. 2·61	13. 3·49	14. 4·01	15. 5·67
16. 20°	17. 40°	18. 5°	19. 25°	20. 14°

21. 23°	**22.** 37°	**23.** 41°	**24.** 55°	**25.** 60°
26. 70°	**27.** 73°	**28.** 75°	**29.** 77°	**30.** 79°

Exercise 68 *page 76*

1. 2·424 cm	**2.** 4·207 cm	**3.** 2·66 cm	**4.** 1·35 m
5. 1·95 m	**6.** 3·77 m	**7.** 2·5 m	**8.** 7·2 mm
9. 0·88 mm	**10.** 0·63 mm	**11.** 6·4 cm	**12.** 9·2 cm
13. 8·2 m	**14.** 9·6 m	**15.** 3·12 m	**16.** 11·8 m
17. 20·3 m	**18.** 25·7 cm	**19.** 36·09 cm	**20.** 65 cm

Exercise 69 *page 77*

1. 4·86 cm	**2.** 1·53 cm	**3.** 1·224 cm	**4.** 1·269 mm
5. 4·83 mm	**6.** 3·56 mm	**7.** 4·9 mm	**8.** 0·97 m
9. 0·63 m	**10.** 0·26 cm	**11.** 0·28 cm	**12.** 6·9 cm
13. 5·5 cm	**14.** 5·4 m	**15.** 4·28 m	**16.** 13·5 mm
17. 12·4 mm	**18.** 18·8 m	**19.** 35·6 m	**20.** 22·89 m

Exercise 70 *page 78*

1. 15°	**2.** 20°	**3.** 29°	**4.** 27°	**5.** 23°	**6.** 28°
7. 37°	**8.** 35°	**9.** 32°	**10.** 18°	**11.** 57°	**12.** 62°
13. 73°	**14.** 61°	**15.** 78°	**16.** 70°	**17.** 58°	**18.** 49°
19. 66°	**20.** 71°				

Exercise 71 *page 79*

1. 19°	**2.** 23°	**3.** 28°	**4.** 31°	**5.** 18°	**6.** 24°
7. 34°	**8.** 42°	**9.** 32°	**10.** 34°	**11.** 54°	**12.** 63°
13. 65°	**14.** 49°	**15.** 71°	**16.** 66°	**17.** 61°	**18.** 64°
19. 70°	**20.** 78°				

Revision exercise D
page 80

1. 63 cm, 61°	**2.** 18 cm, 42°	**3.** 40 cm, 58°	**4.** 22 mm, 70°
5. 14 mm, 61°	**6.** 9 cm, 13°	**7.** 3·276 cm, 55°	**8.** 18 mm, 60°
9. 21 mm, 68°	**10.** 6·776 cm, 52°	**11.** 3·83 m	**12.** 1·41 m
13. 3·5 m, 1·94 m	**14.** 6·9 m		